POG

WEATHERING THE STORM

SAMANTHA THORNTON

Mereo Books

1A The Wool Market Dyer Street Cirencester Gloucestershire GL7 2PR
An imprint of Memoirs Publishing www.mereobooks.com

Pog: 978-1-86151-388-5

First published in Great Britain in 2014
by Mereo Books, an imprint of Memoirs Publishing

The address for Memoirs Publishing Group Limited can be found at
www.memoirspublishing.com

The Memoirs Publishing Group Ltd Reg. No. 7834348

The Memoirs Publishing Group supports both The Forest Stewardship Council® (FSC®)
and the PEFC® leading international forest-certification organisations. Our books carrying
both the FSC label and the PEFC® and are printed on FSC®-certified paper. FSC® is the
only forest-certification scheme supported by the leading environmental organisations
including Greenpeace. Our paper procurement policy can be found at
www.memoirspublishing.com/environment

Typeset in 11/15pt Bembo
by Wiltshire Associates Publisher Services Ltd. Printed and bound in Great Britain by
Printondemand-Worldwide, Peterborough PE2 6XD

If you are inspired by this book please give generously to Maggie's, a charity I hold dear to my heart. Please either send a cheque to the address below or go to my Just Giving page at http://www.justgiving.com/Samantha-Thornton2

Thank you.

Maggie's Centres are warm, welcoming and uplifting places that provide free practical emotional and social support for people with cancer and their families and friends. They are places to find answers to your questions; places to meet people who understand what you're going through; places to find the hope and strength you need.

maggie's

Registered Office: Maggie's, The Stables, Western General Hospital, Crewe Road, Edinburgh EH4 2XU Registered Charity Number: SC024414
www.maggiescentres.org

50% of the proceeds from this book will be donated to Maggie's

For my darling husband Guy.
My rock, my lover, my friend.

For Tom, Atalanta and Marcus.
My boulders. Your unconditional love helped
me keep on fighting.

*What the caterpillar perceives is the end
to the butterfly is just the beginning.*

Chinese proverb

Prologue

This book is a giant thank-you letter from me, Pog, a nickname I was given early on in life by my family for reasons that have been long forgotten. It is the only way that I can really give thanks to all those who helped me on a long and arduous battle back to wellness. I am so totally indebted to you all. Many of you are named specifically as headings for chapters but there are also those people who were there along the way, all part of this amazing timeline that is life and I am truly grateful to you all. However, over and above being a thank-you letter, this is also a book of love.

On so many levels my journey has been an expression of love. My husband, my children, my stepson, my siblings, my parents, our old Nanny, friends, relatives, people working for us. When the chips are down you realise that life is purely an expression of love. Love in all its shapes and sizes and glory.

There is also a third element and that is endurance, perhaps even courage. Maybe I have the lead role in this but my husband Guy is not far behind, as are our chidren.

What is courage? It is facing the enemy in the trenches and heroically saving a fellow soldier when under fire. It is the fireman saving peoples' lives from leaping flames on a daily basis. It is escaping from an oppressive regime with only the shirt on your back, abandoning all that you have ever known.

But there is also a more common requirement for bravery that nearly all of us have to face at some time: when we are confronted with our own mortality. My story is about that and I hope to tell it with as much love, thanks – and courage – as I am able.

Was I born with courage? I was certainly born with a silver spoon in my mouth. But courage, no. I have always been afraid of almost everything, including the boogy man under the bed.

Every night when Nanny put me to bed we would have to look under the bed, in both the cupboards and even in all the drawers of the chest of drawers, just to check that the room was boogy man-free. This was in the safety of a beautiful country house, set in a huge garden surrounded by a large farm. Not exactly the dangerous part of town! As I grew older my two brothers, Grant (older) and George (younger) would torment me with Dr Who, ripping the cushion away from my face as I hid from terrifying daleks, who were going to destroy the world as I knew it.

As we hit early teens, Grant was always getting into terrible trouble with our parents and I too would be chastised as I would always end up crying for him. I would get so anxious my stomach would hurt and on several occasions it was thought I had a 'grumbling appendix' and nearly ended up having it out.

George bore the brunt of Grant's older-brother status and was submitted to doing terrifying ordeals that luckily I could get out of as I was a wimpish girl who would cry. Needless to say if George escaped Grant's 'manly' games, he ended up playing 'girly' games with me: a joyful choice of 'dressing up', which entailed blue eyeshadow; or 'secretaries', which meant carrying our desks to the bottom of the garden and setting up an office at the back of a huge herbaceous border hidden by large lilac bushes. Poor George. What a choice!

When I was nearly ten and George nearly seven, Camilla came along and then Miranda three years later, so Nanny was kept busy and the nursery remained a haven where we always knew she would be: the constant monotony of her clicking knitting needles and Radio Four playing in the background, a never-ending source of harmony.

Outside the nursery there was discord. The hedonistic seventies reaped havoc on many families and ours was no exception. The divorce changed us all. The sense of betrayal and abandonnment was absolute. I was too naïve to understand and nobody tried to explain. The confusion, the pain and the ignorance was utterly overwhelming and chaotic and I think that it was at this point in my life that I pledged that I would never, ever give up on anything or fail. An obvious recipe for disaster!

Our nanny was the embodiment of harmony. She was as solid as a rock. She never left us but came with us to Paris when my mother moved there with the younger children, even though she never understood or spoke a word of French. Our nanny hated France. She was so lonely but it never ocurred to her to leave and come back to England because we needed her. She was unstinting and unconditional in her love. When she eventually retired she stayed part of our family and came to us for lunch every Sunday.

Sadly she has not lived long enough to read this book but one thing we all cherish was her unstinting, unconditional love. But it is this quality of harmony in her that I saw, and loved, and that I have always looked for elsewhere.

It was important in my career as a specialist in Old Master Sculpture at Sotheby's auction house in London. Some people relate to music or poetry but my tipple was, and is, the fine arts. Looking at a painting sends me on a journey to oblivion, where everything around me ceases to exist and the brushstrokes take on melodious, soothing caresses on the canvas and the juxtaposition of pigments create such harmony and bring me such peace, to a point that there is a genuine physical expression and my body will totally relax. It can even make me cry.

I was always too fearful to try it myself and it wasn't until I was ill that I finally started creating through the medium of sculpture.

This all sounds rather like Dorothy in the *The Wizard of Oz*, on a kaleidoscopic adventure to find herself, a book I used to adore and I am so grateful to Christine Kidney for helping me make my own journey into a book. Thank you. I just wish I had those fab ruby shoes!

Finally I would like to thank my parents. It's easy to dump blame on parents and step-parents and of this I am guilty and, yes, at times their actions caused me great pain but only because I didn't understand and was so frightened by that ignorance. They have loved and nurtured me unstintingly over the years doing what every parent does – the best they can.

CHAPTER 1

Guy, George and Burgs

'Feel from the centre of your chest. May all beings be happy.' Not only could I *not* feel the centre of my chest but, more to the point, I wasn't exactly sure where or what the centre was. I was also hampered by the fact that Captain Haddock and a terribly good-looking Bedouin were charging across the inside of my closed eyelids on camels heading straight for a supermarket checkout counter manned by Brad Pitt.

Thus my meditation career started. I collapsed into fits of giggles and won the sanguine sighs of Burgs and George as they glanced at each other and wondered what the hell they had taken on. Perhaps the giggles were a good release for what was a very serious and frightening time in my life.

How had I come to be sitting cross-legged on a cushion in my sitting room at home trying to feel various parts of my body in an attempt to still the mind and release all my negative energies in order to help heal my cancer?

In January 2002, when I was thirty-five years old, I found a rather large lump under my right armpit. In fact even before the lump under my armpit there had been a couple of weird bumps in the back of my neck that I had chosen to not think about. I went to the doctor, the doctor did the blood tests, the results were an unusual type of toxoplasmosis and I was duly sent off to a toxoplasmosis specialist, who told me that total rest was the solution.

Well, total rest with an eighteen-month-old and a three-and-a-half year-old is not easy even if you are spoilt rotten and have a nanny to help you look after them. I was in fact feeling very ill most of the time and sometimes could hardly even climb the stairs at home.

Added to this, I felt desperately unhappy and unable to cope with my wonderful life. My darling husband Guy suggested we ring up some great friends who conveniently live in the Bahamas to see if they would have us to stay, which miraculously they agreed to and so that is where we went with the children and their nanny, for ten days.

Well, after ten days of sun-kissed heaven, strolling along pink sandy beaches and lazily watching sandcastles being constructed, the lump vanished.

A month later, it returned. I was loathe to go back to the doctor as I knew I had been prescribed total rest to allow my immune system to fight the illness but I did go and see my obstetrician for my annual check up.

As soon as he asked me how I was, I burst into tears. You have quite a special rapport with the person who has brought your children into the world. So I snivelled and explained how awful I felt and that it was because of this rare form of toxoplasmosis. At which point he looked at me and said, 'But that's impossible. I tested you for that when you were pregnant and you have had it in the past and can't have it again. I think we had better speak to your doctor.'

I think I felt relief that it was going to be something else that perhaps would need medication and not just total rest. It certainly never dawned on me that it could be anything sinister.

The advice after the subsequent appointment with my doctor was that we have the lump removed. A supposedly easy procedure, all over in fifteen minutes. However, when I came round from the anaesthetic, I was not totally surprised when the surgeon told me it had been rather more complicated than they had thought (nearly two hours) and that he had never seen anything like it in all of his career.

This was music to my ears, as to my mind, if a very experienced surgeon, who had seen many malignant tumours, did not recognize mine as one, I was presumably home and dry. Two dear friends, Sonali and Cameron, came to visit and, my, how we laughed about the 'alien' being removed and that at least I wouldn't have to shave my head like Sigourney Weaver did for her part in the film of that name (in those days I had rather pretty long, blond hair).

I was in hospital for a couple of days and Guy brought the children up to London to see me, which in hindsight was a huge mistake. They were traumatized seeing me hooked up to a drip and with tubes coming out from my armpit draining fluid and the goodbye was really horrible for all concerned.

However it was a taste of what was to come.

The results came about a week later and Guy and I were still so convinced that there was nothing to worry about that I drove up to London by myself. Having found a space for the car, I ambled into the clinic, up in the lift to the third floor, headed calmly to the bland off-white waiting room with the usual drinking water dispenser and then into the consulting room. I remember the desk was set at an angle in front of a large window. After the conventional greetings, the toxoplasmosis specialist started talking about the lump, saying that it wasn't toxoplasmosis after all but that it was this other disease called lymphoma, and that I needed to see another specialist who was conveniently situated just down the hall and that he would be only too happy to take me to see him.

His voice started to sound more distant and I found my attention lured away to the cityscape behind him, which was framed by the window.

I think I am fine but I am taken aback as this is obviously not as simple as I thought it was going to be and deep down inside, fear starts to flutter its wings.

Outwardly I behave quite chirpily, as I think that I'm finally going to be able to take some medication and start feeling better.

'Oh, thank you,' I say. 'How kind. You don't have to bother, I'm sure I can find it by myself if it's a nuisance.'

I was secretly pleased that I was going to see someone else as I hadn't particularly taken to this man. He insisted on escorting me, as if I were at a new school, being shown where the history class is by the geography teacher.

I have very few recollections of the next moments.

The next specialist introduced himself as Maurice Slevin, an oncologist specializing in breast cancers. I was numb. It was all a mistake. I had been shown to the wrong 'classroom'. I know I asked what lymphoma was and I know that he told me that it was one of the good cancers to get. I remember him being kind, incredibly kind. Almost scarily kind. He said we needed to get more results and to come back the following week. I left that room feeling like I had just had a vest packed with explosives put on me with no means of taking it off. I was a walking bomb. I was a walking bomb who had to drive home without detonating.

We live eighty-five miles west of London near Swindon, which normally should take about two hours from central London. On this particular afternoon there had been a crash on the motorway so the cars crawled along like a serpent of red break lights for another extra hour and a half. That's a long time to be alone with your cancer, even if it is a good one to get.

The following week, Guy and I headed back for the rest of the results on his vespa. It's the best way to get about town and I have always loved riding pillion as it's a wonderful way to look at all the buildings and admire rooftops. It is amazing how many beautiful sculptures are on the top floor of buildings or on the roofs.

Guy had suggested the car but I so craved that feeling of freedom, whizzing in and out of the traffic without a care in the world. I was completely in denial.

The news was not great. The lymphoma was a very aggressive non-Hodgkins lymphoma. It had reached stage 4 and had progressed into my bone marrow. So not such a good one after all. However, the expression 'when it rains, it pours' could not have been more apt. As we were given this chilling news, the heavens opened with a huge clap of thunder and lightning and torrential rain. Mr Slevin took one look at our crash helmets and the lashing rain against his window and we all burst out laughing.

This was followed by small, nervous chit chat until we reached the crux of the matter. He advised me to be treated under Professor Andrew Lister at St Barts Hospital in the City of London, who was at the forefront of lymphoma research in England and who was my 'best bet'. Luckily we could do this as we have a flat in London, where Guy has his office.

Usually one is treated much nearer to home but who was I to query 'my best bet'? I hate shopping around and in some instances that is a very good thing in my opinion, particularly when you are ill. Do you get millions of quotes from different builders when you want some work done? Or do you just get a couple, like one of them more than the other and then just go with them, hoping your instinct was correct and that they will see you right? That is what we did with Professor Lister. I put my life in his hands right from the start and would not see other oncologists for second opinions as I knew it would confuse me and thus weaken my belief in his being able to heal me.

The tests continued and the news seemed to get worse and worse. Guy and I are still not sure if they realized at this stage that there was another completely different lymphoma hiding behind the aggressive one or whether that one only became apparent when we got the aggressive one into remission.

Getting back on that vespa was a much more sobering affair. Neither of us had cried in the consultant's rooms and it wasn't until we were cocooned into the privacy of our own crash helmets that the tears started to roll. Both of us were silenced by the sheer enormity of the situation, unable to speak. With the visor down, the roar of the traffic around us, and incapable of talking, I hung on to my husband's waist for dear life all the way back to the flat.

The next step was to tell the family.

It's a funny thing, denial. Everyone deals with shock in different ways. My father (traditional old school) talked about the weather and food he had eaten on recent trip to Spain. Very odd, considering his wife had successfully combated breast cancer. When he was confronted by Guy the following day he was able to explain that he had thought stiff upper lip was the best way as otherwise he would cry. Thank goodness Guy was able to tell him that was exactly what I needed and a very weepy walk with my father around the garden followed. My mother, whose husband had sadly not made it with bladder cancer, announced that at least I would lose weight when I told her of my misfortunes and impending high-grade chemo treatments. In fact, she returned to France and I didn't see her again for six months.

My sister Camilla was utterly amazing and selfless and got on the next flight from Argentina, where she was living, and came to look after me for the next eight months. My brother George stepped in at this point and asked me if I remembered his friend Burgs. Well, yes, I did, sort of. He was totally crazy, did extreme skiing in Chamonix and had set up a business with George selling clothes to the great and the not-so-good in skiing and surfing resorts. Their business motto had been 'Make madness a way of life'. And they had. Little did I know how much he had changed.

Burgs, it transpired, had moved to Bali to design and make the clothes for the business and had since sold it in order to learn the art of meditation. He was doing a lot of work with healing, and alternative and complimentary medicines.

According to George, he had recently returned from Bali and was in England starting to teach meditation. He was helping a German man who was very ill with cancer. George thought I should learn to meditate with him. 'No way, José', or words to that effect, was my reply.

Now, it was one thing that my darling brother wanted to *ommmmm* his way through life, but I was different. I wanted to eat, drink and be merry and forget all about this hiccup of an illness and just pretend it wasn't there. I was aware that I would have a rough ride through the chemo but otherwise I just wanted to be the best mother that I could be under the circumstances and get on with life. *At no point whatsoever did that include sitting on a mat in silence and confronting my life.* I was totally happy being on the run.

So much for what I wanted. Guy and George fixed a day with Burgs and he came down to the house to see me. In fact, it was a comfort to see someone I knew (albeit not well). It was also a relief to see that he was totally unfazed by the prognosis and completely at ease with everyone else being totally fazed.

His absolute calm was very soothing. It is not my place to tell Burgs's story, although I can say that it is an extraordinary one and you should definitely read about him on his website, theartofmeditation.org. There are very few Westerners who have attained his level of meditation. The healing work he has done with his master, Merta Ada in Bali, is truly humbling. However at this point I wasn't really thinking about any of that. I was just feeling threatened.

It's funny how sometimes you can feel totally threatened by the one thing that might be your salvation. We talked. I cried a lot and he listened to my rantings, which I think covered most of my then thirty-five years. The good thing was that he wasn't a stranger and although it was quickly turning into a therapy session, it didn't appear to be because he was my brother's friend.

We tried to do some meditation but that's when Captain Haddock put in his appearance. The upshot was that he couldn't really do anything to help me until I had done a basic course in meditation with him and that we needed to do that soon, as the chemo was starting in about three weeks. Frankly I didn't really comprehend why I should do this before the chemo started but both he and George were adamant. Their knowledge on 'alternative healing' was totally bewildering but their insistence that I should go into 'chemo battle' as well prepared as possible did ring true and soon appointments were set up for me for live blood analysis to ascertain what vitamins / minerals / herbs / supplements would best arm me for the way ahead.

I was becoming increasingly anxious about the way things were turning out as I still didn't understand that this was all about taking the bull by the horns and helping myself. I was pretty ferocious with Guy when it was decided that I should go to a cottage on the farm in the next couple of days and start a silent retreat of meditation with Burgs and George *for one week.*

Burgs had talked to Guy privately to give him a pretty honest appraisal of where we were and how much this meditation could help me and therefore him and the children as well. But I was looking for sympathy, not help. I was a victim and wanted pity, 'the poor, poor you, have a cup of tea and a cuddle' type of thing. Not boot camp. I felt as if I was being put in detention for doing something bad. Didn't they realize that it wasn't my fault? That destiny had landed this illness on me and that there wasn't a single thing I could do about it?

How wrong I was. I went kicking and screaming to the cottage a couple of days later, all my abandonment issues coming to the fore, sobbing my guts out as I had to leave my children and thus in turn 'abandon' them. Of course the joke was that if I didn't get better I'd be abandoning them for a lot longer than a week but I couldn't begin to compute that.

Meanwhile, Guy stayed back and kept the home fires burning, the appearance of a 'normal', everyday life for the children and the money coming in to pay the bills.

CHAPTER 2

Camilla and
Professor Lister

That week in the cottage was hell. The cottage itself was charming enough, with a little wood-burning stove in the living room, a kitchen with a cosy table around which we ate in silence, two bedrooms and a bathroom for Burgs and George. My older brother Grant lent me a bedroom in his farmhouse next door as he and his family were away in London. Looking back on it I guess I just didn't understand anything. I was in denial about the gravity of my disease and hoped that lots of red wine and chocolate would sort it out.

Meditation was anathema to me. Sitting in agony cross legged was bad enough. To remain there unmoving for forty minutes was nothing short of a bad joke. Multiply that by eight times a day with breaks in between for chi kung and rest and meals of my new 'cancer diet' and I have to say that I felt very sorry for myself. I broke the rules in the evening by finding a book and reading it. For some reason that made me feel better. You are not meant to write anything or read anything, as it clouds the mind.

This is also why you do not speak. Of course Burgs speaks; he is the teacher and you can ask him valid questions but otherwise it is just another excuse for the mind to wander. Well, in a perverse way, it made me feel in control of the situation ... clearly by not adhering to the well-trodden path followed for centuries by yogis, I thought I knew best. When I wasn't counting down the seconds to the point I could uncross my legs, I was venturing outside to go and sit on a hill from where I could see my home. Or I was sobbing.

I was totally blind to the fact that my brother had stopped everything to come to my aid. Burgs had downed everything he was doing to be there for me. Camilla had left her life in Argentina to come and help me and the children and Guy was being just his amazing self and keeping everything together for our family. You couldn't really be more at the centre of attention if you tried and still I was feeling sorry for myself!

There is a fine art to teaching meditation. The beginner needs something on which to latch the mind, whether it be a mantra, a pond of water, a circle of colour, whatever. Burgs uses the body, which is an ancient meditation practice from the Burmese arm of the Buddha's teachings and enables the yogi to still the mind on parts of the body whilst simultaneously re-aligning the body's software, which ultimately (when re-balanced), can heal the hardware. There are myriad different teachings and techniques for meditation and I am certainly not the person to try and explain them. However I can describe what Burgs was trying to teach me during that first week of medititation in the cottage leading up to my first 'breakthrough'.

In order to try and calm the mind, Burgs focuses on the breath and the point at which it enters your body, ie the tip of your nose. (Try it, it sounds simple but after a couple of breaths it's easy to find your mind wandering off.) You do this for a couple of days (which sounds impossible and quite frankly nearly is!). The structure to the day is simple. 5.30 am: wake up. 6 am: meditation followed by exercise and breakfast. Teachings at 9 am, followed by meditation, break for twenty minutes, meditation and then an hour of chi kung. Chi kung is a Chinese healing practice with roots in martial arts. Using strong awareness and mindfulness you do slow-flowing movements with deep, rhythmic breathing in order to cultivate the 'chi' or life force within the body. Lunch, rest. 2.30 pm: meditation, break, meditation, questions and talk, meditation, break for supper, teachings, bed. The structure is all part of the disciplining of the mind. Once the mind starts to be focused and more disciplined it begins to become more harmonious and more objective towards the chatter of your thoughts. More distanced. They become a background sound to which you try to pay no attention and when they do grab you again (oh, I'm so miserable that my boyfriend dumped me twenty-five years ago, ouch, that bit on the left side of me really hurts), you notice that you have lost your focus on the breath and start again. The focus is not to buy into those thoughts and get caught up in them. Once this disassociation with the noise kicks in and your mind has become more harmonious (two days of nashing of teeth), you head into your body. Again, this sounds ridiculously simple. It's not as if you are learning Chinese or anything. It's just your own body! My thoughts exactly, but that is where I was wrong.

This next meditation is called 'Body Parts' and

17

Burgs introduces what you are doing as follows: 'Use the harmonious mind to work through the body part by part letting go of all the bad reactions inside the memory, all the unwholesome energy in the body. Feel each part of the body in the moment with mindfulness, feel it changing with wisdom …' OK, so you spend a few moments on the breath just so you calm the mind and get focused and then Burgs leads you through the meditation guiding you around your body. First off is the top of your head, the right side, the left side, the back, the front, the eyes, nose, cheeks, jawbone, teeth. So far, so good. Then the neck, the different parts of your neck, the muscles, the throat, the bones of the spine. 'Try and perceive the different textures of materiality.' Hold on a minute. What?! You're only about five minutes into a forty-five minute meditation and your legs are aching, your knees are uncomfortable, your back is screaming and you're longing to just get up and get the hell out of there and you cannot feel a thing in your neck, let alone differentiate the 'different textures of materiality'! And so it goes on. 'Whatever sensations appear, feel them as they are. Feel the characteristic and feel them changing in the moment. Pressure, tingling, hot, maybe the hardness of the bone? Don't try to create a feeling with the mind. Don't strain the mind as it will produce stiffness and pressure in the body'. All so seemingly simple until you realise that you have absolutely no connection whatsoever with your mind and body and that Chinese would definitely be easier because you wouldn't have to try and face your body and a sick one at that.

Whenever your mind wanders off you bring it back to where it is meant to be focused and just stay in the moment being with whatever feeling comes up. In other words level-mindedness: or, mindfulness.

Whether you are feeling a sense of pain or bliss, the reaction should be the same. You are merely the observer, objectively feeling rather than giving a running commentary on 'my left knee hurts, oh, the lump in my neck hurts. Oh no, that must be my cancer. Or, oh, my stomach feels all hot, what does that mean?' No, no, no. Equanimity is king. The teachings are that if you put your harmonious mind to each part of your body and see it for what it is, the imbalances that are there will re-balance and, simply put, a perfectly balanced body is a well body.

The strange thing for me was that I couldn't feel anything that I was supposed to feel when I was prompted to do so and was temporarily obsessed by parts of my body that hurt the moment I sat down in the cross-legged position. George and Burgs would sit at each meditation effortlessly and at the end of a session George would ask a question about what he had felt in his lungs, for example. Meanwhile I was desperately trying to work out why I could feel the pain in my knees the moment I sat cross legged on the mat but when we eventually reached them going through the body in the meditation I wasn't able to feel a thing. Moreover, any pains I did have (and there were many) all went the moment I stopped meditating. It was as if my body was going on strike every time I sat down to meditate.

Oh, the array of emotions I went through: anger like I have never known it, frustration, hopelessness, self pity (copious amounts of that) and pure rage at Burgs and George. I became obsessed. My hatred of them was absolute and yet still I sat there trying to feel *something, anything,* when I was meant to. When my awareness did allow me to start feeling the parts of the body I was meant to be feeling, it was completely outside my body to the left of me, as if I had a double sitting beside me. Very confusing. Was it frightening? I don't remember fear regarding the meditation. I remember utter confusion. How could something as simple as sitting on a mat being with 'myself' be so utterly horrible?

The fear that consumed me was not over the meditation itself. In the silence and the stillness I caught my first glimpses of the reality of my situation: I might be going to die and I couldn't see how sitting cross legged with a tsunami of emotions washing over me was ever going to help. Cue more tears. If I was going to die I wanted to be with my children. Cue sobbing.

So much for equanimity. In fact I did several retreats before I even began to understand what Burgs really meant by equanimity.

However as the week progressed and the wild chattering of my 'monkey' mind began to abate, a strange thing happened. I began to get an occasional glimpse of peace. These were few and far between and the wildness of my thoughts became all the more pronounced but it was most definitely there. A suspension in nothingness. Total tranquillity, a brief absorption with the present, so very fleeting and yet so utterly beautiful and perfect (which of course vanished the moment I reflected on how beautiful and perfect it was).

George warned me that day three is the worst. Well, I say days three and four. It is so very hard for me to describe how difficult it was for me to be with myself. I am sure some people find it a doddle but I had such a strong hatred for the situation I found myself in, I just couldn't stand being me! So to not have any diversions was tough.

On day three my mind really started playing

hideous games with every long-held emotional issue coming to the fore and seemingly every pain I had ever encountered was being relived and I genuinely started to convince myself that it would be better to just jack it all in, drink myself to death (at least fun) but Burgs kept a very close eye on me and cajoled me through the never-ending forest of my chaotic mind.

Day four was worse than day three, if that's possible, and I just ended up on auto pilot struggling to get through each session. My body started to completely sieze up so I sat on a chair but even I began to recognize that it was nothing to do with the exercises and sitting cross-legged, but all to do with the thoughts in my head that I was forever latching on to and obsessing about.

By the evening I had cried so much that I think I was genuinely dehydrated. However I realized I only had three more days to go and that I was over the worst. Oh, the fickle mind. I instantly started to feel a bit of a hero and was rather pleased with myself for what I had survived! Days five and six I hung in there, getting these occasional oases of peace that I mentionned earlier, and day seven was the last day so I was suitably elated to be going home.

After a week of doing this work twelve hours a day, you cannot just be expected to get into your car and drive off. You would probably crash into the first oncoming car or in my case be so angry with the world and the universe that it would bring an entirely new meaning to the words road rage. This was why it was very important to go through the closing stages of the week's retreat, which starts the afternoon of day six and into day seven. In the simplest terms, during the course of the week the meditations allow your subconscious to slowly reveal itself, bringing up various memories and traumas that are conveniently deeply buried in your psyche so that you don't have to face them in your daily life. It would be very unwise to leave the retreat in such a raw state and it is therefore really important to 'close down' that level of awareness and exit the world of our dreams knowing that it is a work in progress (in my case). After a couple of sessions you then break silence and start talking far too much and promptly get a ferocious headache.

It was day seven that I finally 'popped' and somewhat miraculously 'opened my chakras'. In tantric and yogic traditions of Hinduism and Buddhism, the seven chakras are the energy centres in our bodies through which our vital energies flow. I had no intention whatsoever of opening them. I had only just learnt about them for the first time in my life at the beginning of the retreat, so it is fair to say that I have no idea how I did it but I think that that is the moment when it occurred to me that there just MIGHT be something to this meditation malarchy.

We went through a closing meditation: *metta*. This means 'loving kindness', which you give first to yourself and then to others, both friend and foe. I questioned giving myself loving kindness first as I thought it rather selfish but Burgs compared it to the oxygen masks in an aeroplane which you put on yourself before being able to help anyone else properly. This was an eye-opener to me. I had always thought it truly dreadful and unbelievably selfish that you were supposed to think of yourself first, particularly in a time of emergency. Patiently, Burgs explained to me that you cannot help others if you don't help yourself first. A very small penny dropped.

We did more metta and I started to feel very ill. So ill in fact that I must have changed colour as quietly Burgs asked me if I was all right. 'No,' I said. He stopped everything and asked me to lie down with my head near his legs and my body stretching away from him. He started chanting and holding his hands above my head. He told me to just concentrate on my breath and to feel my body. I started shaking and shuddering and my body started taking on a life of its own; I began making the 'fish/snake' or 'worm' manoeuvre they do in break dancing – not something that I am well known for. All the while Burgs chanted and all the while I concentrated on my breath and tried to stay focused on the cool air hitting my nostrils as it descended into my lungs and then the warm air as I exhaled it. My body contorted and spasmed in the most extraordinary way. This lasted for perhaps ten minutes and when it all stopped I was utterly exhausted. Then I just lay there and slept.

Afterwards Burgs explained to me that my body's energies had been blocked but that this was a start of opening up the 'energy paths' and that now we could really start the work at hand. Start? I thought I had finished! Such is the path of the reluctant yogi.

So, feeling some sense of achievement, I returned home and started with renewed vigour the cancer diet that had been prescribed to me by Burgs and George, and which was being administered by Camilla. The chemo was starting in a few weeks and I had to go into battle with all guns blazing.

That lasted about a day. I *hated* the cancer diet. I was a red wine-drinking, meat-eating cheese fanatic. All out the window. No alchohol, no sugar, no caffeine, no meat (except white meat, fish or game once a week, maybe), no wheat, no dairy, the minimum of fruit (because of the natural sugar content). What did that leave? Basically vegetables and brown rice.

This was a diet that was advised by the Bristol Cancer Help Centre, now the Penny Bohn Cancer Care, which was a charity set up for patients to help themselves as much as possible when fighting cancer. And of course it makes sense: when you are battling a serious disease your body needs to use all its potential energy to combat it. Therefore you hardly want it to be using most of its resources just to digest meat and cancer loves sugar so an obvious foodstuff to eliminate.

However none of this makes sense when you don't want – or indeed can't – make sense of anything that's happening in your life. My sister Camilla, nicknamed Pill, used to greet me in the morning with a freshly squeezed vegetable juice, consisting of, for example, spinach, cabbage, beetroot and root ginger. I also had another mug full of something which we called green goo but which was in fact a powder full of every ounce of goodness you can find in green vegetables, sprouting pulses and seaweed but it wasn't fresh, hence why I did both. Lunch might be quinoa and roasted vegetables, and dinner a rice and vegetable curry. All in fact delicious, but not very tempting when you're craving lamb cutlets. A vegetarian herself, Pill researched diligently recipes that might please me and all she would get was tofu thrown back at her. I still can't eat tofu. In short, I felt rather bullied! However, deep down inside I knew that I was incapable of doing all this by myself. I knew it made sense as I would never have had the will power to do it on my own. I needed to be bossed around. Thank the Lord they could all be bothered to.

Meanwhile, Burgs and George were sending me off to see a host of people to set me up with complimentary medicines prior to Chemo Day. Friends also advised me of alternative healers they knew and so I was kept very busy. Most of this work was in an effort to get my body into shape for the onslaught of the chemo.

This was war and war needs strategies to be fought on many different fronts with as many different weapons as possible. Equally, a war was never won just with weapons. The soldiers cannot fight without food, transport, clothing, medicine and good leadership. Was I in charge? No, I think I was just some flotsam ebbing and flowing with the tides. I'm not very proud of the fact that I was so incapable of taking my own life in my own hands but thank goodness Guy, George, Burgs and Camilla were.

One of the 'alternative healers' a friend put me in touch with told me it was my fault I had got ill. That in some cases cancer is slow suicide. I left in a state of total shock. Two of my girlfriends still swear by her and even take their children to see her for various allergies, aches and pains but I have to say that even now as I write this I feel the shock of being told something so brutal. How can it be all right to have a one-hour consultation with someone who has a chronic disease and it be appropriate to tell them it's all their fault? How can you possibly know the mental state of the 'patient' in that one hour? I mean, it could have completely tipped me over the edge if I had been a bit madder than I already was.

The alternative/supplementary route is a minefield. So much so in fact that after helping me, George became a mentor with the Health Creation Mentor Service to help others with cancer who wanted to find alternative and holistic ways to work in conjuntion with Western medicines but felt lost and needed guidance and support.

I hated meditating. I hated my diet. I was now taking thirty 'alternative' pills a day (it eventually reached sixty). I hate taking pills. I had been told this mess was all my fault and I hadn't even started chemotherapy. Who needs enemies?

At this point I was permanently furious and took it out on Guy and Pill with both barrels. I was so frightened of what was happening that I never stopped still for long enough to realise that I was still blaming everyone else and not taking the reins for my life into my own hands. Surely it is better to be master of one's own destiny rather than flotsam on the tide of life? I just hadn't worked it out yet.

Chemo day had to come and it did. We knew it would be bad but we didn't know how bad. A bit like childbirth, really: it's probably best not to know too much as otherwise you would never do it. Guy and I trecked to St Barts hospital by St Paul's Cathedral. We had started making a habit of lighting a candle in the small church of St Bartholomew the Great next to the hospital. It is an extremely beautiful and spiritual church, not in the grand sense of the Gothic style with soaring vaults and vast pointed arches, but intimate and serene with the rounded arches of the earlier Romanesque period. It was founded in 1123 by Prior Rahere who also founded the hospital and has always been a place of prayer and solace for the sick.

I was undergoing CHOP, which is a very strong chemo and not only did I have to do it intravenously but also into my spine, because the lymphoma had progressed into my bone marrow. Hospitals are hospitals but the outpatient oncology wing hadn't had a refurbishment yet. It was Dickensian. There was an undeniable smell of public loos with disinfectant trying to mask it. The nurses' station was in the middle of the room and seated patients were given their 'poison' on the left and those on beds on the right. The chairs were the plastic ones that you get in village halls but if you were really lucky you could try and get the soft chairs with arm rests. If not, you just had to make do with a pillow on your lap to rest your arm on. I think the room instilled the most fear in me.

However one thing I will say is that the nurses were truly remarkable.

I saw Carol long before I met her, and was amazed by her unflagging energy, her never-ending kindness and the upbeat way she chatted to all the patients. There must have been twenty or so of us all hooked up, with relatives hanging around (or sitting if they had managed to find a chair). She and all the others were always bright and cheerful and they never had a moment to rest. A lady with a trolley of sandwiches would come round periodically. I really couldn't believe it when the lady with the wigs came round.

The intravenous treatment was just about manageable. It's hardly OK but you just get on with it and nowadays they have plenty of anti-sickness drugs. Some of these are administered intravenously and others are given to you orally on your first day. In fact, you are given a wheelbarrow load of drugs to take home. Also, mouth washes to use and ulcer creams.

Then you wait for your chemo into the spine. You

get a bed for that and in my case a curtain, as I was a wimp and needed drugs to do it. Actually, I am now feeling sick and tears are welling up in my eyes even as I think about this.

In the course of all my tests prior to chemo day, I had to have several lumbar punctures. This is very painful and for some reason that I have still yet to completely understand, you can only have a local anaesthetic (which never seems to work). I became so intolerant to pain that I was given a drug which is surely not the date rape drug, but works not dissimilarly. Inasmuch as you are awake but it fools the brain and you cannot remember anything.

It is a very bizarre feeling as your body knows instinctively that something is very wrong but you don't know what. So you curl up into the foetal position and they mark the place on your spine where you are going to take the hit. You then get the local anaesthetic and the other drug (not always available) and you have the chemo administered. This is dangerous. Firstly, if they do it wrong you can be paralysed; secondly, they have to take out the exact same amount of spinal fluid as that of the chemo they are going to put in; and, thirdly, this fluid affects your brain. After you have had the dose it is imperative that you do not move at all for at least half an hour. After this you are free to go home, having been told it will affect your sight.

Did I make it home before being sick? Guy collected me and we went to my friend Debby's house first, where another girlfriend, Jessica, also swung by to give me a kiss and a cuddle. I was sick with them.

We then drove straight back home to the country. And then the pain started.

How do you try to convince your three-and-a-half year-old and eighteen-month year-old that Mama is OK when you are throwing up and in screaming pain? I've never had a migraine but by God I now respect people who get them. But even the worst migraine occurs without having your spinal fluid (this is the same fluid up to the brain) sucked out and then replaced with a very strong poison. You genuinely cannot move the pain is so horrendous. But if you are throwing up, you cannot help but move.

It takes three days for the pain to go. Not every time, but most. You are spent. We got very good morphine-based drugs to combat it but that was the most mentally challenging part to this round of chemo. Every three weeks I had to mentally prepare myself for voluntarily putting myself through untold pain. That's the strange thing about chemo. Most of the cancer patients that I have since talked to regarding their treatments describe how mentally challenging it is to take a drug that makes you feel awful when up until then you weren't feeling bad (which was slightly different in my case as I did feel unwell).

Imagine what it feels like when you can tick off another chemo day. That's why you prep yourself for the next round. That desire to get through.

They told me my hair would fall out quite quickly and, boy, did it. It started to come out after about ten days and I had a wonderful dance to go to that my aunt and uncle were giving. I had had my long hair cut short in preparation and was now the proud wearer of shoulder length hair, which nearly got left behind in the curlers the night of the party! Fortunately, Pill helped me and disaster was averted and I had a full head of hair for the evening, even though large clumps did fall about me when I danced. Two days later I tried to wash it while having a bath and huge great chunks just came out getting stuck all over my body and getting tangled in my hands. I started to panic and Pill came running but it got worse as we tried to dry me. Literally, it had taken on a life of its own: there was hair everywhere. More sobbing. Eventually we got the situation under control and decided to shave what was left off. No, that's not true; we had been advised not to shave it off as the stubble can cut you and cause infections as your skin is far from normal with the chemo. So we went down to the kitchen and Atalanta and Marcus sat on my lap whilst Pill cut off what was left with the kitchen scissors and the children dried the tears that slid down my cheeks. Atalanta, with the wisdom of a sage, said, 'Mama, don't worry. I will love you anyway and it will grow back'.

The finished result was actually a relief, I suppose, because the trauma was over. The children were delighted and asked if they could paint my head, which they duly did, skipping around the kitchen table with renewed excitement as they laid out the obligatory 'splat mat' and their wares of colourful paints and paintbrushes. Laughter and life resumed as I was told to 'Sit still, Mama, otherwise you'll blotch it' and all the colours of the rainbow dribbled down my face and neck. Always look on the bright side of life.

I had one more week until the second chemo and Burgs and George said I needed to do another retreat.

Like anything new, you can't master a new subject immediately and I was no natural at mediation. It was going to be a long battle for me to achieve any kind of equanimity. My eyesight had gone very quickly and I could no longer drive. It was important for me not to get any infections, so another week in the cottage was organized before hit two of the chemo. More time away from my family. I dreaded it but equally knew deep down that it was helping me. As I still couldn't feel the majority of my body I couldn't fathom whether it was helping me physically; however, mentally there was no doubt. So much so that Guy was really keen for me to go! (The man is a saint.)

It didn't seem any easier this time. There were now four of us: another man, who was very ill with MS, had joined us. The 'boys' stayed in the cottage and I slept in Grant's farmhouse next door as again he wasn't there. Lending the cottage and the house wasn't as easy for Grant as it sounds as he was extremely nervous that George and I were going to be turned into saffron-robed baldies strumming tambourines and drums up and down Oxford Street. I think our father was pretty nervous of that too in the beginning. Grant, his wife Vanessa and their son Fred didn't use the farmhouse very often and it was pretty spartan. He didn't even have any alchohol in the house. I should know, as I looked everywhere.

The desire to create a distraction, and not to be doing what I *should* be doing (sitting peacefully on a mat) was completely overwhelming. It's not as if it was very difficult but for me it was nothing short of all the Labours of Hercules put together. It felt as if every cell in my body was screaming. Every neuron in my brain was synapsing (if that is indeed what neurons do) and my mind was going bonkers throwing every toy it could get its hands on out of the proverbial pram. 'Inner peace' (see films *Kung Fu Panda 1* and *2*) was a long way off.

I struggled on and we got to day three (Wheels Fall Off Day) and by mid-afternoon I decided to run away. I was so ashamed that I could not even manage one week of silent retreat meditating, which, after all, could be seen to be a pleasurable time of rest, that I knew I could not go home. So I packed a bag and reckoned that if I walked a bit down the road I could hitch a ride to Heathrow and go to St Petersburg and the Hermitage Museum or Venice, depending on whichever had the first flight. I craved beauty. My soul settles in the face of beauty and abides in peace. I craved escapism. I felt so ashamed by my failure. For years I had had an issue about being able to escape from anything and everything and was unable to leave the house without my passport. So that was not a problem. It was safe in my handbag.

George caught me. I got nabbed just as I was leaving the house with my luggage, tiptoeing to the road. It wasn't very adult really and is quite amusing in hindsight but it wasn't exactly the behaviour of a mother in charge of her life. I absolutely hated him in that moment.

Burgs sat me down beside him in the garden and we talked. My past, my present, my fear of a lack of a future. My terror of death. Tears rolled down my face and my shoulders heaved for what seemed like hours (it probably was) and I thought my sorrow was going to break me in two. But it didn't and I think it was the defining turning point in my life.

I slept and the next day I started meditating again, only this time there were little patches of clarity and those aforementioned glimpses of peace and tranquillity. It was like two butterflies occasionally coming to rest on my shoulder. So fragile, so tenuous and yet so beautiful and all I had to do was watch. They came to me when I was still: I couldn't catch them when dashing hither and yonder in search of them.

Another penny dropped.

CHAPTER 3

Daddy, Martine and Kim

Six months is a lifetime in a capsule when you are going through intensive chemo. As my eyesight had deteriorated rapidly, driving was impossible and some days even reading was difficult.

Talking on the phone was exhausting. After a conversation it really felt as if my life force had been sucked out of me. I called it the Dyson Effect. As a result, I spoke to fewer and fewer people and resorted to emails when I felt like it. Friends and friends of friends wrote wonderful letters or just sent kind cards always reminding me that everyone was gunning for me.

We battened down the hatches. George came to the house at least a couple of nights a week. We gave Burgs an old car on its last legs and he was therefore able to come and see me once a week and give me healing and sit and meditate with me. Guy worked in London three days a week leaving me in the loving hands of Camilla and the house and children were looked after amazingly by Kim, the lady who looked after the house, and Martine, the children's nanny. Friends came and went and some brought food: wonderful dishes, lovingly home made, either for me (on my strict regime) or for the family to eat at weekends. Both were a godsend. My stepsisters Sophie, Emily and Arabella organized for a weekly box of organic fruit and vegetables to be delivered, which was fantastic for all the juicing we did. We all got into a rhythm.

Preparation for the chemo soon followed; then the chemo then the fallout after the chemo. Building strength back up. Preparation for the next hit.

Any delays in treatment and the whole protocol would take longer. In my case, winter and the cold weather brought more infections, which I found harder to fight. However we had a battle plan and we stuck to it as much as possible. I meditated every day with recordings from Burgs and even started to meditate sometimes in the evenings in the children's bedrooms after I'd kissed them goodnight. Each child had a turn and they grew to love me sitting cross legged in the dark beside their beds whilst they went off to sleep. They didn't really understand what I was doing (I'm not sure I did) but I wanted them to feel that they were not excluded. One evening I was meditating downstairs and Atalanta slipped quietly into the room and wrapped her little body around the back of me like a cat and fell asleep. Once, when Marcus was a little older, he came up to me and blew on my closed eyes and said, 'Mama, are you there?' Truly adorable. I would often release pent-up emotion and cry and that was difficult for them to understand that that was all right – good, in fact.

Weekends were tricky for Guy. He worked very hard all week and of course Camilla needed a break at weekends, which meant that he never got to relax. Tom, my stepson, needed collecting from boarding school two hours away, whichever exeats he was not spending with his mother. Joan Field, also known as DON (Dear Old Nan), who had looked after me and all my siblings for thiry-five years, always came for the day on Sundays. Sundays wouldn't have been Sundays without her. Even with all the delicious food cooked up by friends we needed help as quite often we wanted to see some friends or family in order to get a bit of a break from our insular existence and to make life feel as normal as possible.

Through word of mouth, Hilary turned up like a

fairy gothmother to cook for us on Sundays. She was wonderful with the children and cooked like a goddess. That Christmas she even sacrificed her own family lunch and moved it to dinner so that she could cook our lunch for me. She turned Sundays into the world of the Sugar Plum Fairy and when the children had their birthdays in November, meringues miraculously turned into swans with either black or white feathers, ships of oranges laden with jelly sailed off plates and even the 'healthy' food took on star like qualities and was all therefore gobbled up. I am so grateful to her. It is a long time ago now and we are probably a distant memory for her but to us she will always hold a special place in our hearts.

One of the most difficult things for me to manage was my guilt over my children. I wanted to be the primary carer for my children and as my strength failed, I felt more and more of a failure. As a result I would promptly over-do it trying to be with them and then collapse causing everyone to get cross with me and the children to get upset.

This craving to be 'normal' got me into many scrapes. I had absolutely no dignity as a patient.

I am sure Camilla will be howling with laughter at that sentence. How she suffered. She got it in the neck almost every day and if she didn't, Guy did. If I was in pain I would lash out. If I was exhausted, I would lash out. If I felt terrible or just jealous at everyone else's abilities, I would lash out. In short I just took all my frustrations out on those two and Camilla was the one giving me zillions of pills (all alternative) as well as the medical ones and the vegetable juices that made me retch. Add to that a mouthful of ulcers and the fact that everything tastes as if you are eating tinfoil. Of course she got it in the neck!

We did go out to dinner occasionally and then Pill was so kind, spending time helping me wrap my baldness in beautiful scarves, trying to make me look less like Kojak and more like one of the models from Yves Saint Laurent's 70's Russian-inspired collection. Everyone tried to be so kind but it was very difficult. Firstly, there were very few things I could eat and secondly, what the hell do you talk about? The weather? People would ask me what I did. What could I say? Those were some of my loneliest times, when in fact I was surrounded by people. Occasionally my guard would come down and I would talk about my situation. This was often a big mistake. The poor fellow guest would increasingly take on the look of a caged animal and find some excuse at the earliest polite moment to find a reason to get up to get something, or go to the loo, or just flee and I would go home feeling so guilty that I had ruined their evening. I was always taught that one should never discuss politics, religion or health at dinner as it might cause huge arguments and therefore be insulting to the hostess; and there I was banging on about all three (NHS, Buddhism and meditation, and cancer). A couple of years later we were invited to a long weekend birthday bash in Switzerland and I was so insecure about my conversation skills that after dinner the first evening I hijacked two very dear friends and Guy and two bottles of wine and said that if we didn't assign me an 'occupation' by the end of the evening, I was going home. We duly spent the rest of the evening working out what I could say I 'did' in life and the results were wonderful. In fact I have used them quite frequently since:

Q: What do you do?
A: Drugs and occasionally my husband.
Or
A: Actually I've retired.
Q: From what?
A: From smoking.

The following evening when I used the last answer (without batting an eyelid or bursting into giggles) I had the best fun I had had in years.

Being bald is strange. You catch yourself in the

mirror and then you get the shock of your life, particularly if you have no eyebrows left and very few eyelashes. I bought a wig but the children were horrified and I hated wearing it as it itched so much and my internal body thermostat was so bonkers that within minutes of putting it on I nearly fainted. Scarves were the best option for me. Big long ones that I wound around my head to get some 'volume' where hair might have once been. Camilla was brilliant at it, I less so. The only setback is that these turbans tend to move. They tilt, or wobble, to be exact, and they can feel very heavy on a bad day. You are hideously self-conscious about it all and, bizarrely, you don't want to put people ill at ease. So I would carefully wind myself into my 'bedouin' look if anyone was coming or I was going anywhere.

This changed somewhat after a lunch with Leo, a very dear friend who insisted on me taking off my wobbling turban as it was beginning to make him feel sea sick and he wanted to see what I looked like bald. Well, I was horrified at the notion but he kept on insisting and so I took it off – in the middle of a restaurant in Chelsea, I might add. I thought the world was going to gobble me up I felt so ashamed. And then he told me to look around. Had anyone even noticed? I rather timidly acknowledged that it did appear that the universe had not come to a grinding halt because of how I looked. And then he told me I looked beautiful. I shall never forget that. It was so uncalled for but changed my perspective forever. I knew Guy loved me warts and all and would accept however I looked but for a friend to accept me and even compliment me, that was very poignant. He then of course berated me for being so daft and told me that half the people walking down the Kings Road shaved their heads anyway so what difference would it make if I did. That did it. I walked out of that restaurant without my turban and never looked back. Peculiar though it may sound, I had been really fearful that friends weren't going to still like me without my long blond hair.

Guy would collect me after my day of chemo and we would drive home to the country with the seat down as much as possible to try and keep my spine as flat as possible in an attempt to ward off the killer pains. Each time we were warned of my becoming neutropenic and the complications thereafter and given all the emergency numbers we might need.

Neutropenic is when you have an abnormally low number of neutrophils in your white blood cells. It means that you are more susceptible to infections, which without prompt medical attention can become life threatening. It was just a word to us and we didn't realize what its full implications could mean.

I remember the first time well as a friend had come to visit with her two children and we suddenly noticed that my right arm, which had a mosquito bite on it, had started to become bruised. Over the course of the afternoon this bruising turned a startling black and started moving up my arm. I felt fine. Well, everything is relative, but we knew that if anything like this happened I had to go to the hospital straight away. Martine was leaving for the day so Camilla took charge of the children; my friend was going home with her children and Guy was working in London. So we called my father to ask him if he could drive me up to London to my hospital. Guy was in charge of calling the oncologist to tell him of my impending arrival. My father duly arrived and off we set in his car. Just before we got onto the motorway, we got a frantic phone call from Guy on the loud speaker saying, 'Fred, on no account drive to London. You must take Samantha straight to Swindon Hospital. You do not have enough time to get her to St Barts. She might die before you get her there.' Not what a father wants to hear and frankly not what the patient wants to hear either. We dashed to Swindon A & E and became increasingly worried as they simply didn't appear to know what to do with me. But after long three-way conversations with the doctors on the ward in London, Guy and the doctor on call in A & E, it transpired that I was not in grave danger and just needed a course of antibiotics. My father is truly amazing in times of crises but I think we were all shaken by that.

There is a much-loved green armchair in our kitchen and it is where Martine or I would always sit and read with the children whilst preparing a meal, or where they would lie covered with a blanket if they were poorly but didn't want to be alone upstairs in bed. It is where I spent most of my life if not in bed. I was getting weaker and weaker and could not walk very much any more so would just 'hang out in the green chair'. The kitchen has an aga so is wonderfully warm. This is another chemo hazard: you are always cold (I used to give Guy the fright of his life in the mornings as quite often I would sleep in a big woolly hat). So, when everything took a nosedive, I was in my usual pew.

One evening, just before bed, Guy jumped up and said he was going to take my temperature. It was over 105. That requires immediate action. Camilla stayed at home with the children and we got in the car and drove to the nearest A & E whilst Guy spoke to the doctors in London who once again reitereated that 'you don't have time to get to London'. Perhaps we did it wrong, but at the time it seemed the right thing to do.

Maybe we should have called an ambulance, in which case you go straight to the front of the queue but, again, hindsight is a luxury. I can't imagine what it must have been like for Guy. Firstly, there was the wretched car park. At least at night you don't bother to pay for a ticket but it's miles from the entrance if you are feeling as ill as I was. When we arrived we gave our details, saying it was very urgent and that I was neutropenic with an infection. They looked at us as if we were from Mars.

The oncologists in London were extremely concerned and demanded to be put on to the doctor in charge via Guy's mobile. The receptionist would not oblige. It got very fraught and eventually we were put into a cubicle and a young doctor arrived who thankfully had the good grace to admit that he didn't know what to do in these situations. This meant that at least he was prepared to speak to the oncologists in London. They were getting pretty irate and saying to Guy in no uncertain terms that without immediate and vast quantities of antibiotics I might die.

I was now so unwell that I didn't really know what was going on but on the first occasion I remember being 'stored' in a passageway and being very aware that if this was the end it was a lousy one. It wasn't.

However I had septicaemia and it was very serious. It happened a second time and that time at least they put me in a room to avoid any further infections but I have clear recollections of dried blood on the floor (not mine). Apparently, according to the consultant a couple of days later, in both cases there was real concern that they weren't going to be able to save me and each time I recall being surrounded by nurses with fans blasting me and wet towels being laid over me as my body contorted with convulsive shivers. I remember that cold so well and yet my temperature was going off the radar it was so high.

I was in solitary confinement for ten days on huge quantities of antibiotics. Both times I lost ten pounds during that critical twenty-four hour period, such was the onslaught on my body and I could hardly move afterwards as the convulsions caused all my muscles to spasm. It was a miserable time and the only good thing about it is that sometimes it pays to be pig-headed and have enough dogged determination to hang around.

My father and stepmother would come and visit and put on the plastic protection kit and Guy came every night to visit after he said goodnight to the children and then he would just lie on my bed with me and we would watch television together but even then Camilla would send him in with a plastic bag full of all the supplementary pills I was meant to be taking.

This was hideously painful as my mouth, throat and entire digestive system had become covered in ulcers. Now I knew why we were given wheelbarrow-loads of mouth washes and ulcer creams when I started the chemo.

Those were dark days and it was the hospital cleaning lady who would make me smile. She was so upbeat, always chatting away about recipes for cake baking; you couldn't help but see the light with her around. A friend of ours, who had successfully beaten Hodgkins Lymphoma, had told Guy that whatever happened, whatever the situation, just make that your 'normal'. It was wise advice and we really tried to adhere to it.

Once the septicaemia was under control, it was just a question of waiting for the body to become strong enough to start making white blood cells and then I was allowed to go home. The difficulty was then trying to get myself strong and well enough to take another hit of chemo, which would inevitably land me back at square one. Snakes and ladders with high odds.

This was why the meditation was starting to earn such a secure place in my tool kit for survival. I did it every day. It was my mental workout. Burgs had given me CDs of his most basic meditations and I did them religiously. If I didn't, Guy would notice that I became increasingly anxious and less 'grounded' and would ask me when I had last done it and to go and do it immediately! I still couldn't 'feel' my liver, lungs, gall bladder –well, most of my organs, in fact – but it gave my mind something specific to latch on to instead of the negative mental aerobics it would otherwise occupy itself with.

I had my thirty-sixth birthday that summer and Guy gave me the most wonderful present. Of course I didn't know what it was and he told me I had to find it. A seemingly lovely idea but I was so exhausted and as the morning wore on and I couldn't see it, the crosser and more exhausted I became, exacerbated by the fact that everyone kept following me around. I began to feel like the Pied Piper.

There was Marcus, Atalanta, Camilla, Tom, Martine, Kim and Guy all loitering behind me wherever I went. They were all so excited. The last straw was when Guy suggested that I looked out the dining room window. I completely blew a fuse and ranted and raved about how dirty the window pane was and how absurd that nobody could even be organized enough to get the window cleaners in! I never even saw what was on the gravel in the background. In the end they took me outside and I just burst into tears.

Outside was the fulfilment of one of my dreams: a classic navy blue 1972 Fiat Cinquecento with soft top, wrapped in a huge red satin ribbon with a bow on the top and festooned with peacock feathers all ready and waiting for me to see it.

I now ask myself what it must have been like for those helping us. It must have been very hard for Kim and Martine. They didn't know what situation they were going to find when they came to work every day and always had to put on a big smile whatever. Martine was incredible with the children and even took them to stay with her parents in Cornwall when things got really tough.

And so it went on, each day a new dawn. Each day new hope. There was a rhythmn to it all and it was a military operation with all the battle plans that that involves. At no point did I ever want to give up. Sometimes I despaired but there were too many people sending their love to me for me ever to contemplate not battling on. Sometimes it was lonely because nobody understood what I was going through. And the worst thing is you know how serious it all is when everyone is nice to you all the time.

One last recollection I have of that time is with my

father. Guy was in London and I don't remember where Camilla was but I was alone one evening and couldn't bath the children as I wasn't strong enough to get them in and out of the water. So I rang up my father and asked if he could come and help me. He arrived and duly undressed them and bathed them while I lay resting on the passage floor outside the bathroom door chatting to him. After a period of merriment, bubbles, splashing and general laughter he quietly said, 'This is the first time I have bathed a child.' A sobering reflection from a father of five. This illness was changing us all.

CHAPTER 4

Kate and Lois

The chemo came to an end in the autumn. After that we just had to wait and see if it had done its magic.

It was very strange having to get back to normality. One of the first changes was Camilla saying goodbye and moving to South Africa. On the one hand I was chomping at the bit to be strong enough to run my own life again and on the other I was miserable to be saying farewell to this incredible sister who had dedicated eight months of her life to us. By the time she left, she was emotionally exhausted from giving so much of herself and was trying to sort out some big issues she was having to come to terms with and I think she hoped that a different country would help her.

Families are like mobiles that you hang from the

ceiling: each family member is weighted at the end of its own arm but they are all intrinsically attached to one another with the overall balance of the mobile dependent on each arm being independently balanced. This illness had caused all sorts of shock waves through my family and the mobile was not at all balanced.

It was a very difficult time for Pill and I just wish I had been able to repay her. Instead she sought help from those who had the strength. I wonder now whether, if I had not fallen ill, would I ever have reached this deep bond with Camilla? I don't know. It's under pretty extreme circumstances that something like this occurs. I am so blessed to have her as a sister.

In December we understood that the chemo had worked its magic and that Christmas was a truly wonderful time of celebration. However, it was short lived as the results from my January check-up showed that I had another lymphoma called follicular lymphoma. Now this is a nice slow-growing one in comparison to the stage 4 Large B cell lymphoma that we had retreated into submission but it has a nasty habit of triggering off aggressive ones if you happen to be unfortunate enough to have one lurking. A devious bastard, basically.

This is a grey area in my memory as I do not know

to this day if I had always had the follicular lymphoma and just hadn't focussed on it or if it was a new arrival to the party. It may seem bizarre that I don't have all the facts but frankly it doesn't change the big picture either now or then. Guy and I were devastated as were all our loved ones around us. It was such a roller coaster ride of shock, amazement, surprise and another large dollop of fear. One minute we were merrily going for a check up and the next minute we were back to square one again. More snakes and ladders.

The professor said I couldn't do another round of chemo yet as it would kill me; it was too soon after the last round. What to do? It seemed we were back at square one and somehow it seemed all the worse as we now had a certain amount of knowledge under our belts. Sometimes ignorance is bliss. That blissful family Christmas so full of hope seemed light years away and Guy and I, how did we feel? Numb, dazed, confused.

Some people would have probably gone home and had a nice cup of tea. All those near and dear around me wanted me to get second opinions in America and Germany, a country a lot nearer than America and considered by some to be right up there in terms of success with cancer. My mother was intent on me being seen by oncologists in Paris. In their efforts to help me find solutions everyone was slowly but surely chipping away at my faith in the NHS system, into whose care I had placed my life. Faith and belief that you are doing the right thing is so paramount to staying on top of this insidious disease.

Guy and I decided that I should go on another silent retreat. Even if I wasn't going to be miraculously cured, it was doing me a vast amount of good mentally and enabling me to give myself permission to heal and rest and, if the worst came to the worst, it was helping me face mortality.

I headed off with my sackful of supplements for my first 'public retreat' to a community house that Burgs rented for his courses in Cornwall. I could not have been more surprised to see thirty-odd people who had turned up voluntarily.

The first evening we all talked before taking our vow of silence and it was rather wonderful being amongst all these lovely people who all had their own very valid reasons for needing to do this. I no longer felt alone. I even started to relish the silence. I didn't need to be polite and look after my neighbour when they were crying or make polite conversation with somebody I was probably never going to see again.

I had permission to just get on with my own 'work'. This was unbelievably liberating just knowing that it was all right to be 'selfish'! There was the usual gnashing of teeth whilst trying to settle the mind. but it wasn't just me and I have to admit that by day three I probably wasn't the only one trying to read the ingredients on the loo-cleaning products: anything to divert my mind! Sitting with yourself, confronting yourself and all your demons is no easy challenge.

This is a process of trying to 'purify' the mind. Refining your character. Defusing the charge carried in the body from old memories stored in the mind and body. Concentration and serenity overcomes the overwhelming feelings of restlessness and the sense of feeling ill at ease. Mindfulness/attentiveness overcome ignorance (the willful ignoring of things as they are) and the feelings of laziness, sloth and torpor. Finally equanimity brings an acceptance of things as they are. OK. That's the theory.

In practice it's reluctantly sitting on the mat again having just busied yourself making yet another cup of tea in the break. You feel really pleased with yourself because you've just concentrated on your breath for about three minutes but then you have an overwhelming urge to get up and leave. Not only that, but the person who is sitting behind you innocently sniffing (probably going through some tearful, emotional turmoil) is about to have your fist in their face because that noise is making you SO ANGRY and guess what, there's another thirty minutes to go before Burgs is going to close the session.

There were more lectures from Burgs, some of which I had heard before and hadn't really understood; now it was starting to resonate. As a creature of habit, I was settling into the rhythm of the retreat. I knew what to do and what to expect and felt more in control. Famous last words.

Even though I had never done a standing meditation before it didn't set off any alarm bells. That is until I blacked out, nearly flattening a rather petite lady in front of me. After we broke silence at the end of the retreat much was made of the event and I was likened to the drunken character, falling like a felled tree at Holly Golightly's drinks party in *Breakfast at Tiffany's*.

Once Burgs knew I was alright all he said of the matter was, 'at least you finally got out of the way.' He was not alluding to the aforementioned lady but to my mind. At the time I didn't really understand what he meant but laughed anyway … but after a certain amount of reflection it became clear that although it's not exactly the usual way of 'calming' the mind, it did the trick.

What was beginning to resonate was 'the nature of impermanence'. All things are impermanent and, depending on molecular structure, have a longer or shorter life span. If one can begin to grasp this fact, one can begin to see that nothing is permanent and therefore start the long process of letting go of everything because in essence there is nothing to hold on to anyway. The rising and passing of matter. Molecules, cells, atoms, subatomic particles; it all lives and dies and is changing all the time. In which case, by definition, my body and therefore the cancer in my body was impermanent. The cancer cells were living and dying just like any other cells and that realization was incredibly empowering. Perhaps, just perhaps, I could zap them.

Burgs had a bigger plan for me and this involved going to Thailand. In addition, Lois, a wonderful therapist whom I had started going to about a year before I was diagnosed, suggested that I attend a residential course, called the 'Hoffman Process'. I think I agreed to all of this because I didn't want to disappoint anyone: despite being weak after the chemo and my fear of leaving the children again, I still wanted to please. I was also terrified that my children would think me a failure if I didn't at least try what was being suggested.

So we hatched a plan. I would go to Thailand first for two weeks, meet up with Burgs, and then on my return I would submit to the Hoffmann Process. After that we would see what chemo I should do. I would only agree to go to Thailand if it was for a maximum of two weeks. I really did not want to go. George offered to fly with me, as he was concerned that I might do a runner. How right he was.

I had already got the address and telephone number of the mother of a friend of mine in Sri Lanka and had thought I could escape there (it looked sort of midway homeward-bound on the atlas). Not really very logical as that would not be returning to my children but logical is not a word many people would use to describe me.

Burgs chose Thailand for good reason. With his enormous knowledge of Oriental medicine and before coming to England, he had been working with some Canadians out there who specialized in alternative healing methods and alchemy: the art of transmuting metals, in this case gold, into a powerful medicinal powder. My understanding is pretty sketchy about Canadian and American law, but, simply put, their governments are lobbied by the hugely powerful, big pharmaceutical companies who want to keep the monopolies on their (in some cases very expensive) medicines, thus making it illegal to practise many alternative healing techniques using natural minerals, natural herbs and plants and natural vitamins, which cannot be patented. So many healers from these countries go to other nations like Thailand or Mexico to set up alternative healing centres, where it is legal.

I had put my life in both Professor Lister and Burgs's safe hands. The Prof had managed to put my aggressive cancer into remission and now Burgs was prepared to try and help me seek another route with the second lymphoma which might conceivably avoid further chemotherapy (which we knew I couldn't do at the moment anyway so what did I have to lose?). These were people whom Burgs thought might be able to help me and therefore I trusted his judgement implicitly.

How was this supposed to work? In simple terms, if you can put your body in the best shape possible, by means of detox, cleansing the blood, taking myriad lotions and potions, maybe, just maybe, it will be able to use its own artillery (the immune system) to tackle the unwelcome cells. It does happen. Whether it could happen to me was another matter.

This is not a cheap undertaking, even though Thailand is cheaper then Europe. My mother, who had been somewhat shocked by my very deteriorated state when she came to visit me just before my last chemo session, was very pro my going, even if it only made me stronger. She offered to pay for it and Debby, the wonderful friend in whose sitting room I threw up on day one of chemo, gave me her air miles for the flights.

Atalanta's godmother, Kate, my childhood friend whom I have known since I was two years old, also came up trumps and assured me that she would visit her goddaughter and keep an eye on her, Marcus and indeed Guy. In the event she was so good at entertaining them all while I was away that when I used to hear about their happy times as I put in my weekly telephone call, I got rather jealous!

So we rejected any further western treatments temporarily and on 15 March 2003 I set off for Thailand, to the island of Koh Samui, and the Kwan Jai Health and Wellness Spa. In order to pass the time of day, I kept a journal of my time there.

The clinic was in downtown Chaweng and was nothing like the island paradise that all my friends had fled to when we were eighteen. It was seedy, with back-to-back cheap hotels on the beach and endless stalls on the road selling fake designer stuff crowded with middle-aged Europeans drooling over young Thai women and the occasional 'lady boy'. My hotel room was fine, a sort of concrete bungalow with a thatched roof and it didn't really matter what the dining room was like or indeed the food, as I never ate there. George and Burgs both had rooms further back off the beach, which was very reassuring, even if I did only see them sporadically. The clinic was a ten-minute walk down the beach, which, in fairness, was very beautiful.

However, you then headed back onto the Chaweng drag and the clinic was opposite the local gym. From the outside the clinic looked like a mass of rather badly placed tropical potted plants with glass doors opening into a hair salon with entrance hall and desk. This was all in wood, with a shiny marble polished tiled floor and Thai wooden furniture ... Randy was in charge of dealing with us as and when we arrived, either off the street or pre-booked in. He was totally bonkers and even looked like a mad professor, the Stephen Hawking of the 'wellbeing world'. He was the eletro-magnetic/gadget king of the operation and was perpetually fiddling with all the machines and indeed inventing them. I had never met anyone like Randy before in my life. I'm not sure we were able to communicate on the same level as he was a 'transcendentalist' and communed with 'superior powers' (which I clearly was not a part of). However, he had a big, kind heart and was always there for us even if he did tell us he was 'communing with other beings in the universe'. Very talented, clearly.

Peter was the Big Boss, whom I met when I first

arrived and who was very keen to tell me that his first wife had died of lymphoma, which was why he had made it his life's quest to try and find alternative healing for cancers. He was very insistent that I might have to stay longer if I was serious about healing myself. Yes, of course I wanted to get better but no, I definitely did not want to stay longer. He became quite agitated about how I had to see this mess I was in for what it was and what hard work I would need to put into it if I was going to reap any rewards in healing. Frankly, all I wanted to do was flee the room and pretend none of this was happening. Every fibre of my being was trying to slam on the brakes and avoid reality. Next to his office was Will, a quiet unassuming man who specialized in Ayurvedic medicine, an ancient Hindu medical tradition. Burgs was working with them daily but not at the clinic so in fact I rarely saw him at all. George had decided to do a detox at another venue the other side of the island so had rented a motorbike and whizzed around and popped his head around the door when he felt like it. I was so jealous of his freedom with that motorbike.

Shalom was the hero of the everyday workings of the clinic. He was Thai and was in charge of all the local staff and spoke the best English of them all. He always had a smile on his face and yet worked thirteen hours a day with only two days off a month. His power base was the fridge beside the fish tank on the first floor and he made certain that you were taking all the drinks you had to be taking. He noted down your pH balance results which you had to check frequently to make sure you remained in an alkaline state. He also worked out your timetable either for massage with one of the blind masseurs, who miraculously never seemed to trip over any of the machines or the baby trampolene that you bounced on to loosen up the lymphatic system (or for any of the many treatments that took place through the 'glass door'). Through the glass door was the water treatments area where there were only fans and no air-conditioning so that you didn't die of pneumonia. Colonics, saunas, steam room, oil massages, ozone treatments, enemas, alphamassage, oxygen ... *sitting on the loo with the squits* ... all this took place here. Oh, and of course the pH bath that you had to sit in for a minimum of three hours (with no book or anything) to absorb minerals etc.

Back out by the fish tank were four chairs where foot massage (reflexology, which at times was oddly unbelievably painful), bouncing on a baby trampoline (to kick start the lymphatic system, which doesn't have its own engine like blood does with the heart) and various other healing activities took place, mostly involving strange machines invented by Randy, which were either killing parasites, zapping amoebas or destroying the various worms in one's gut. The worst part about this was that ocasionally a fish would die and float to the top and frankly that didn't make life seem any rosier! Next to the offices (where the Live Blood Analysis was done) was the 'Healing Room'. This was a small room of mirrors floor to ceiling, with a black chair in the middle where you were sent to go and confront yourself. Lastly there was a second floor, which was just futons laid out where you were massaged by the blind masseurs and where Randy lived when he wasn't in his shoe-box office inventing mad machines to zap you with, or when he was 'astro surfing', as he called it (I never did find out what that meant exactly).

So this was to be my home for the next two weeks. Some days I was so ill from the treatments that I was driven back to the hotel and partially carried to my room by Shalom. All that stretched ahead was a lonely night feeling ghastly and thinking of the mess I was in. George hung around for a week and then was banished by Burgs as he was my 'crutch' and I had to face this one alone.

This was a multi-layered approach. Ayurvedic herbs,

chinese herbs, minerals, ozone treatments and copious quanitities of vitamin C to bring healing. Machines to zap parasites and amoebas in the blood and then colonics, massages, reflexology, saunas, steam baths and pH mineral baths to expel the toxins in the body. Lastly, the wretched mirrored room was there to look long and deeply into yourself and find acceptance (back to equanimity again).

To do this I had to take a tumbler full of some lotion or potion every fifteen or twenty minutes thirteen hours a day. Half of the time it was some revolting tasting herbal concoction and the other half of the time it was vitamin C – and I mean a lot of it. 60,000mg of it a day. This has to be carefully monitored and balanced so that you remain in an alkaline state. Cancerous cells cannot reproduce in an alkaline state and if they cannot reproduce, logically when they reach the end of their natural life span they are not replaced. Therefore theoretically at some point there will be none left. So every half hour you are testing your pH levels with litmus paper and correcting your pH balance accordingly with another drink. If you are being sick (you spend a lot of time doing that as well) you have some smiling Thai holding the next tumbler of ghastliness by your heaving body, waiting there silently until you down it. I was doing ozone treatments in every (and I mean every) orifice (ear and nose withstanding). Ozone is made up of three oxygen atoms instead of two and has a very high oxidation effect which kills many kinds of bacteria, viruses, yeasts, fungi and parasites in the body. It also helps the liver detoxify and thus purifies the blood and lymph. Also, and perhaps more importantly, it stimulates the immune system, boosting white blood cell function and enhancing killer T cells, which are normally present in the body and which attack cancer cells.

Unfortunately you have to have the runs all the time in order to prevent any toxins staying in your body for too long and being re-absorbed by your intestines. The massages and the reflexology move the toxins from your skin tissues. So, in brief, you are killing off and cleansing everything in your body that shouldn't be there and therefore giving it the very best environment for it to tackle the cancer itself.

Not only was I cleaning up all the mayhem that had been done to my body with the chemo but also deep-seated environmental and nutritional factors that hinder one's wellbeing, a very simple example being mercury from the fillings in teeth.

However, while enduring this, I was so homesick. It overruled everything. I couldn't take on board the fact that if I just embraced what I had to do, I would be home before I knew it. Hell, some people choose to do this kind of thing every year just to be healthy without any chronic diseases lingering over them. Deep down in my heart I knew that this was the right thing to be doing but emotionally I was a wreck and in my mind I was terrified, kicking and screaming all the way.

George took me on a walk down the beach one evening in an attempt to try and explain to me that I just needed to embrace it all and to stop mentally fighting what was being offered to me and I just love the academic metaphors he used to try and make me understand. Not some Greek saga, like Jason and the Argonauts or Hercules and his Labours. He used Asterix and Obelix! Of course I got it instantly. I have always been an avid fan of both Asterix and Obelix and Tintin (which is perhaps why Captain Haddock insisted on putting in an appearance in my meditations). As we strolled down this beautiful beach that I was totally oblivious to, George urged me to understand that I had to go on a 'mission' to get all the ingredients for 'Getafix' to make the magic potion for me and that there would be plenty of hazards on the way and indeed dangers and I would need to ask many people for help. I remember the lapping of the waves and the softness of the sand between my toes as

I started to turn in my mind and take a good and honest look at what I really needed to do. In huge writing in my journal is the word BREAKTHROUGH. I finally glimpsed that I needed to turn into the storm, rather than always being on the run from it.

I say in my journal, 'don't be brave, be courageous'. I wrote, 'being brave is passive and being courageous is actively going towards the problem and taking it full on in spite of being afraid'.

Before George was 'banished' from coming to see me, we had many walks along that beach. I felt huge fear but a great sense of peace when I was with him. This illness had brought us back closer again. We had been so close when we were young but once we went off to boarding school and then when our parents divorced, we had just drifted apart. That family mobile was shifting again.

Being alone and so far away from home, and going through these extreme treatments, made me feel extremely vulnerable to events happening around the world. I felt that the war in Iraq, which had started just before I left, was a huge obstacle between me and my family and when SARS, a strain of pneumonia, started breaking out in Asia, I became convinced I would die of that rather than the cancer, thousands of miles from home. Randy, of course, quoted the Psalm, 'Yea, though I walk through the valley of death, I shall fear no evil' but I am sad to say that that didn't help!

You are meant to get into a rhythm and start enjoying the process of letting go. Finding the faith to acknowledge that chaos is in fact instinctive in nature. Controlling everything is defying the natural balance of the universe. Oh, to this day I find it hard trying not to control everything. Of course it's rather incredible that our minds allow us to believe that we are in control because of course there are so may outside variables that impede this but yes, I was that disillusioned creature who was convinced that there was a 'world according to Samantha'. I would sit in that mirrored room at my allocated time and, to start with, checked out my blackheads; however slowly but surely it gets to you, sitting there, looking at yourself and all your reflections and you start to cry and I mean really cry. Tears from the bottom of your soul.

It is very difficult to explain all this. It is probably even harder to understand. Why didn't I leave? If I was going to end up six feet under, surely it was better to pass the time of day back at home with my children? If not, then the western medicines would have worked and life would resume as normal. Well, that was it, really. What was normal? Deep, deep down I knew

that my 'world according to Samantha' was not right.
On the surface I was one of the luckiest people on
this planet (the cancer notwithstanding) but in my
heart I sensed that my soul/spirit was very sick. I was
slowly coming to the realisation that if by any chance
that had anything to do with my body becoming sick,
then without doubt my body's eventual wellness could
only ever be shortlived if I didn't work on that other
part of me that I don't really have a word for – but
'soul' or 'spirit' is probably the best.

There was no let up. There are the drinks, the
treatments and then the bath. Now, there were many
minerals put into this bath and it had to be a certain
temperature so that the minerals were absorbed through
the skin. I had to be in semi darkness and was not
allowed to read. During those alloted three hours, I was
also given those special drinks, which meant leaping out
of the bath to go to the loo all the time. What was so
astonishing was the colour and scum on the bath when
I got out. It changed to a reddish, rusty colour and all
around the bath was a scum like you find on the beach
left behind by the tide. It was really revolting and yet
truly extraordinary and another of the many ways that
they were cleansing me, the skin being the largest organ
of the body. The worst was the contraption that you got
into to heat up your blood to some godforsaken
temperature to kill off parasites, amoebas – well, you

name it, I guess. I used to pass out every time. I would be given oxygen and then handed another lovely 'cocktail' by a smiling, silent but strict Thai.

The one let up to all of this was the arrival of Sandra and her daughter Sheridan. Sandra was extremely ill with stomach cancer. Stick thin, having eaten nothing since Christmas, this place was her last hope. She was unable to do most of the drinks due to an enormous tumour in her stomach and even many of the treatments but we laughed and cried a lot together and it was beautiful watching Sheridan caring for her mother and having this special (if sometimes awful) time together. Sandra was in tremendous pain and very weak but still she managed to shine. We took a morbid fascination in watching the goldfish slowly die off in the tank in the 'sitting' room, somehow even finding that funny. Perhaps that was done on purpose: another way to confront death, the impermanence of being. Who knows. She became my partner in crime and we soon started to try and get out of doing things. It became rather like being back at school! Sadly, they were unable to help Sandra and she died shortly after returning to London with Sheridan but I was so blessed to have known her and laughed and cried with her even in her darkest hours. We cried on each other's shoulders.

In the end I stayed for four weeks. Why, if I was hating it so much? Good question. Well, firstly I was terrified that I was going to die and secondly I started seeing results in my live blood analysis which were nothing short of miraculous. For the analysis you prick your finger (no more than you would on a rose thorn), the blood is put on a slide and then they look at it under a darkfield microscope. They then see what is happening with the red and white blood cells and check on the bacterial and fungal forms in the plasma and thereby ascertain what lotions and potions should be changed. A dried blood analysis is also taken and then put under a brightfield microscope. This gives a bigger picture as to what is happening in the whole of the body, not just the blood. As the blood goes to every cell in the body to give oxygen and then to take back carbon dioxide, you can get an indication on how effective and efficiently it is working .

I had never seen Xrays of my tumours or scans or anything, so the cancer was still very much a concept but out there in Will and Peter's little office I saw the bastard, there under the microscope, wriggling around on the glass slide. It was a compelling moment. Very powerful. It's you and it. Suddenly you feel as though you can take on this adversary. It's war and you are going to be the vanquisher and not the vanquished.

Every week they did my bloods and every week I saw extraordinary results.

Will and Peter started to show me the images under the microscope of how my 'lymphatic rosary' started to 'fill in'. (This meant that my lymphatic system was unblocking and beginning to function correctly.) The cancer cells started to really diminish. They are very obvious little blighters as their shape is serrated, not dissimilar to a coke bottle top. It became really quite addictive trying to do another analysis just to see if there were less 'coke bottle tops'. The 'canyons', which were white and cancerous, started to turn a pale pink. I should have stayed there for six or eight weeks and I really believe that I could have healed but of course I wasn't at that place of deep understanding and was screaming to go home.

I was beginning to dig deep but not deep enough. Burgs must have seen me having all this put on a plate and rejecting it because I didn't understand. His patience and compassion is unending. He could hold my hand and show me the way but he wasn't going to carry me. I needed to walk the walk myself.

I went home, avoiding the war in Iraq and without catching SARS. But I didn't finish off the job either. The cancer cells had diminished and I thought for a moment that I had nailed it and probably for a day or two I had, so of course I told my nearest and dearest I was better. Ever the optimist (actually I think deluded is probably more accurate). But this wasn't glandular fever we were dealing with. Cancer doesn't let go that easily.

Actually, I didn't go home immediately but went to my mother's house in Normandy. She and Atalanta came to collect me from the airport. It was a truly wonderful reunion but needless to say, that undercurrent of fear was still with me.

It's amazing how quickly you become institutionalized. I was unsure of the outside world and concerned about the strict regime that I had to keep to for ninety days before starting the cancer diet again. This was on top of remembering to take Vitamin C, bicarbonate of soda (to alkalize) every twenty minutes, my myriad supplements and to meditate every day. In the end I became like Little Red Riding Hood with a basket of litmus paper and kit. The children loved helping me and indeed doing their own 'pH' balance tests. It was so wonderful to see Guy and have him hold me in his arms. He had listened to me crying down the phone for thirty days and it must have been so difficult for him as he knew I needed to do this. But hearing someone's distress is never easy – especially across such different time zones. But we were together again and the cancer just didn't seem to matter. But of course, that's not the truth. It did matter. Big time.

Professor Lister had thought I was bonkers to go to Thailand but respected my reasons. However as soon as I was back I was back under his and his team's care. No present action was required. I would have been totally amazed if they hadn't said that, having seen the bloods in Thailand, so it was time to go off and do the Hoffmann Process. I'm not sure how much I can talk about this process as they are imperative that it should remain an unknown for those who go there. The unravelling of the process is all part of it, so they feel that the results are less profound if you know what to anticipate. Lois, who suggested I do the Hoffmann, had finally met Burgs. He had left the Kwan Jai shortly before me, having realised that he wouldn't be able to continue working with Will, Peter and Randy and had started doing meditation courses from the same building as Lois worked in in London. Hearing his name, she had gone along wondering if he was the person I was forever banging on about! For me this was like a good omen and gave me renewed strength to set off on another journey into the unknown.

It was a residential course at a place near Brighton, lasting a week. Yet again I had to leave Guy to hold the fort with Martine looking after the children. It was hard work but very rewarding and I gained some deep insight and learning into myself and others close to me.

Before you go you have to send off a lot of homework about yourself, your relationships, your family and those close to you. Based on this information you give about yourself, you are given a name they consider reflects your opinion of yourself on a badge for the week. Mine was, 'Not Good Enough'. I still have my Hoffmann Process folder with that name on it for some reason. For one whole week you wear the badge and answer only to that name. As with all courses, it is very structured and in this case quite ritualistic.

It was an eye-opener doing the semi-circle thing like you see in the movies: 'sharing'. You realize very quickly that there are some incredibly brave and amazing people out there just trying to survive like you. Some had been through so much suffering and yet they looked so totally normal on the exterior. There is some silence for a day or so but you quickly build up a kind of survival camaraderie, which is rather wonderful. And as you don't know each others' real names there is an effortless anonymity, which is very liberating.

There was one very harrowing moment when I ended up crouching in the corner of the room, howling like a wounded animal with one of the counsellors also crying but – apart from that – it went pretty well!

I like to think that there is always some humour to be had from therapy and indeed this course was no different. There was an 'anger day'. This involved a baseball bat, some pieces of paper and cushion amongst other props but I knew that I didn't have any anger issues so went scampering off to find one of the counsellors to tell them that I could sit this one out as it was only certain members of my family who had anger issues but not me! I was the one always trying to smooth things over and 'keep the peace'. They nodded sagely but suggested that as it was a process, I should just go with it and see what happened. So, being a good girl, I went along with it.

See what happens.

I went ballistic. It was the strangest thing. In fact I can't even remember the exact order of events so will probably get the details wrong. The counsellor talked to us and then we had to write some stuff down on the paper, which we then had to hit symbolically with the baseball bat on the cushion.

As we are being 'led' through the 'process' I start getting hot and cross. I mean, really hot and cross. I started bashing that cushion and those pieces of paper and I just could not stop. After a while everyone else finished and left the room. I was still there sweating, hurting, I had blisters on my hands by this point and thrashing this cushion within an inch of its life. Well, in fact all of its life, as it eventually burst and all the feathers started flying everywhere. At this point I even got the giggles but I still couldn't stop. There was just so much anger in me boiling over. Eventually, I was spent. One of my hands was actually bleeding and I then had to spend an age trying to tidy up all the feathers. So much for Little Miss Meek and Mild!

After the week finished I kept on going to see Lois; everything was whizzing and whirring in my brain as it started to untangle all the emotional turmoil that therapy is so good at dealing with. There is no way that you can do that yourself but I was clearly a totally different person to the one she had first met before I was diagnosed. I felt very proud when she told me that. I was finally committed to turning my life around.

The word commitment was and, to an extent, still is, my *bête noire*. I was always terrified of commitment. I couldn't (and still can't) follow a simple recipe without adding something or leaving certain ingredients out. I actually worked this out recently in a meditation. I am so averse to the potential failure of the food and or indeed anything else that I sabotage it at the outset so I can have an excuse if it goes wrong. Well, at least I've got to the bottom of it and perhaps my food will be better from now on.

When I next returned to Professor Lister I was optimistically hoping that a miracle had somehow happened and that I was now totally in remission but that wasn't the case. It was clear that none of the options open to me were very palatable. Chemotherapy is a blanket term for a whole armoury of drugs: some you take daily, others weekly, and you take the big hitters with a larger pause in between in order to allow the body time to rally. Obviously you can't do this *ad infinitum*, as it will kill you. This is where we were at. If I did more heavy-dose chemo it would only keep the disease at bay for a year. Then I would be able to have one more go and then no more. What did that mean? Well, about four years and then The End. Better than those who are given six months, perhaps, but that would put my children at seven and nine. They would hardly even remember me. This was a constant source of agony for me. I have very few memories of my parents when I was growing up as we were handed over to Nanny and I had always been intent that it would be different for my children. Yet here I was dashing off all over the place trying to heal both body and soul, leaving them with their nanny and potentially dying before I had had a chance to leave an indelible mark in their minds. Memories cannot be taken from you and I lived in agonising fear that I had not had sufficient time to give them enough.

The alternative was a bone marrow transplant, which was unlikely to work as it was not very successful with lymphomas. And then I would be too ill to have more chemo. And, if it were rejected, the death would be painful.

The last option was a stem cell transplant. I couldn't do the auto stem cell transplant, which uses your own bone marrow as I had the aggressive lymphoma lurking in my bone marrow still, but we might have been able to find a donor. In fact, my younger sister Miranda turned out to be a match. The flip side to this was that it was all very new and the death rate was still very high.

Guy and I were so wrapped up in these various alternatives, that we sat at the kitchen table eating supper one night discussing when it would best for me to die in relation to our children's lives. Did we do the chemo and instill in them as many memories as possible before I died, when they were about seven and nine? Did we gamble and do the bone marrow transplant, which would be a complete cure if it worked but statistially it didn't have great results with lymphoma? In which case we were back to square one with chemo as our next option. Or worse, the transplant wouldn't take and I would die and the children would be even younger and have fewer memories. Last but not least the stem cell transplant: again amazing if it worked but if it didn't we were back to the children being super young when I died and not even remembering their mother.

All of this information was being checked, double checked and flipped on its side by Guy late into the night as he sat at the computer researching as much as he could. He was amazing. He never let up. I couldn't take in the information. My brain would just freeze and the statistics were always so depressing and the texts so convoluted but he kept going, saying that maybe we should get a second opinion in New York. I wasn't ready for that yet, though. Again, it was fear. Perhaps unjustified but it was real to me. My stepfather, whom I adored, died of prostate and bladder cancer and he had been treated in London, Paris and America. Actually, it makes me cross just thinking about it as I am convinced (probably incorrectly) that if he had just stuck to one opinion and believed, he might have made it.

Far more frightening, however, was the lump I felt in my breast that summer.

I rang the department at St Barts immediately and was rapidly seen by one of the team who said that we needed to do the CT and PET scans as soon as possible. Once done, you then have to wait for the results which, amazingly, didn't show anything new that we didn't already know about. It was a lump but it wasn't breast cancer and it wasn't the lymphoma. So what was it? I went to see a normal doctor and they said that it could just be changes in my breasts because my treatments had brought on early menopause. The relief was huge but the problem wasn't solved. Then one day browsing in the chemist I saw a pregnancy test and thought, 'Oh no. It can't be. Surely it's not possible'. I bought two kits just to be sure and did the test in a restaurant's loo and nearly fainted when it read positive. I was pregnant. The miracle of life.

As I sit at this computer every cell in my body is screaming for me to get up and leave: to go and do anything else but write this bit down. My heart is racing. I am shaking. Everything is shutting down.

We told the Professor immediately and also went to see my wonderfully kind obstetrician. The baby was just over fourteen weeks old and I wanted to keep it. Every fibre in my being wanted that baby. I became rather evangelical and thought it was a sign from God and that everything was going to be OK. Science saw it differently. For obvious reasons, no doctor can tell you what to do and sometimes that makes it all the more difficult as it is you that has to take responsibility for your actions. All you want to do is to be able to blame somebody else. So, their job is to tell you the facts. In my case there were two main issues. Firstly, due to the nature of bearing a child, cancers grow much quicker, as your body is really firing on all cylinders, which actually enables the cancer to as well.

Obviously you cannot receive treatment whilst pregnant and very often it is too late to turn the cancer around once you have given birth as it has advanced too much. Secondly, I had in all probability damaged the foetus having the CT and PET scans. Neither of these two facts deterred me in any way. It was my miracle and I was determined to keep it, come what may. The fact that I had thought and indeed been told that I had gone through menopause rather strengthened my resolve. I had been told that the strength of the chemo was such that it would obliterate my fecundity but in Thailand they had also warned me that I was doing such a deep, deep detox that there was a risk of reversing that and becoming pregnant and to take precautions as it would be a very bad idea to put my body through this trauma after such a grave illness. Naturally I was such a sceptic I didn't believe them.

Guy started to unravel slowly. It was the first time I had ever seen him do so. His brother had been shot dead in Kenya about a month before I gave birth to Atalanta but even that did not have this effect on him. He wanted me to have a termination. We started to fight. I moved into the spare bedroom and buried my zealous head in the sand. I was convinced that if I terminated the baby it would somehow mean that I was going to die. He argued that if I didn't terminate the baby, I was definitely going to die and he was going to be left widowed with two small children and an infant. It was deadlock. At a certain level I was utterly prepared to abandon my own body (which was clearly faulty) for the sake of a new life. And on another level, I was convinced that I could prove all the statistics wrong and live happily ever after with my perfect family.

It was a very kind aunt of mine who calmly pointed out that I already had a perfect family and perhaps I should try and fight to keep it. I am very indebted to her and as a result of her wise words I started to catch a glimpse of what I was putting my husband through.

We had another very tearful evening, but this time not at each other's throats. I told Guy what my aunt had said and he started to cry and tell me that he had married me because he loved me and he wanted to be with *me*. I cannot really think of a more painful way to be told how much you are loved by your husband. However, reality started to trickle through my veins and in the cold light of morning we decided to terminate the pregnancy.

The date was set. Time had elapsed and the deed needed to be done. Moreover, whilst I procrastinated, tests showed that the cancer was already advancing. Guy took me in to the hospital but there was nothing further to be said and so he left me and went to bury his own deep grief with the companionship of his brothers at a Chelsea football match.

Meanwhile I started to fall apart as the 'procedure' was delayed by four hours. It was, up until that point, the closest I got to 'going mad'. It wasn't of the raving nature. It was the slow breaking of one's soul. I call this my first Gethsemane moment (and I have had one or two) as it made me realize what suffering Jesus endured that night in the garden whilst his friends all fell asleep and he prayed alone knowing what was ahead of him and knowing that there was no one who could help.

Afterwards, I felt as if my spirit had been truly broken and I had nothing left to fight with. There was so much grieving to do but there was also so much joy and laughter to be had with my oh so alive children. It was all so complicated. I felt like a shattered glass and didn't even know how to pick up the pieces let alone glue them all back together again. I began to blame everything on Guy. Then I wanted to blame the doctors. I was lashing out at everyone, everything and anything. If I was in so much pain I wanted everyone else to suffer it too. I was keeping up with the meditation but clearly was unable to 'let go' and 'see the impermanence of it all' and I don't know which of us suggested it first but thankfully we decided to go and see Lois for marriage counselling.

Thank the Lord for Lois! It actually didn't take her long to put us back on track and help us heal our pain and rediscover our deep love for each other.

CHAPTER 5

Debby, Caroline and Stephen Gruenstein

During Christmas 2003 I met someone who was to become a very dear friend. I was introduced to Caroline because she was French (and I speak French) and looking for somewhere to rent in Meribel, where my family has an apartment. As we liaised over this one day, she casually mentioned her sculpture class. Sculpture class! That was exactly what I wanted to do. For many years I had studied and worked in the world of Old Master sculpture but had always been too nervous to dare to create my own work. Caroline was amazing and schmoozed and cajoled the powers that be and managed to organize a place for me on her course. Nine years later we still meet every Thursday during term time. It has been a real lifeline for me; not only have I at last been able to create something of my own but it is wonderful working together with friends and sharing one's weekly problems at lunch. Our teachers Jan and Hywell are incredible, always getting the best out of us and rarely berate me for jabbering away too much to Caroline (normally the case). Curiously, creating sculpture is both a form of escapism and exactly the opposite. In the morning we focus on life drawing, something which I find hideously difficult. But the afternoons are my comfort zone. Working with the human body, creating a representation in wax. I feel as if I am becoming the work. I start to inhabit the figure. Its body is me, not in looks but in the cellular structure and although there is a live model to work from, most of the time I am feeling within my body and replicating that feeling into the wax. This creativity is so soothing. You become so focused with what you are doing that all other external factors fade out. Total concentration. You can really bliss out, actually!

So I started to work with my body, not only with meditation, but also with art. I began yoga in order to heal the aches and pains that I suffered from the chemo into my spine. I was also still paying attention to what I put into my body with regard to food and supplements. Caroline suggested I go and see a kinesiologist she knew, so I ended up with more things to take and I anticipated doing at least three retreats with Burgs during the course of the year. Kate also suggested I go and see a healer called Christa who had been of such invaluable help to her mother while she was battling with cancer. My sight had returned to normal and I was able to drive again so it was easy to go and see her every other week down in Hampshire.

It was becoming a full time job just trying to stop the cancer advancing. At the same time Professor Lister was suggesting further treatments, primarily because the second cancer was going to kick start the aggressive one again and then we would 'lose our window of opportunity'. Whether rightly or wrongly, Guy and I understood this to mean we would be 'up shit creek'.

So with that in mind we agreed to accept Debby's amazingly generous offer of getting a second opinion in New York. She had not only given me her air miles for Thailand, she now had arranged and organised (and insisted that the bills be sent to her) the trip to see an oncologist in the Big Apple.

The efficiency of expensive American health care is staggering. At that time there were only seven PET scanners in the whole of England, so it would take at least a couple of weeks to get a scan. In New York we were doing one the very same afternoon of our appointment. I was so used to the lumbering bureaucratic system of the NHS that this was all a real eye opener, particularly the speed with which we got the results from the tests. In England the results took a couple of weeks to get from one department to the next and then to the prof and his team. In America they just pinged them over via computer the next day. To be fair, by the time I did my auto stem cell transplant a few years later, the NHS had updated its interdepartmental computer systems somewhat.

It is interesting how quickly one gets used to doing these scans and tests without really thinking about the gravity of them and it was very sobering (and fortunate) when I was reminded by the staff at the PET scan clinic not to be anywhere near pregnant women for the next six to eight hours as my radiation levels were dangerous to the foetus. We were staying with a friend who was six months pregnant! That meant going back to the apartment was out of the question until bedtime.

In an ideal world, six hours of shopping in New York would be my idea of heaven but Guy and I always found these appointments and tests really exhausting so the idea of traipsing around shops killing six hours was torture. Who could we call and download all my radiation on for the rest of the day?! Luckily Debby's great friend and organiser of her life, Alexa, who had set up all our appointments in New York, was happy to let us rest at her flat and when she got back from the office we feasted like kings with a Thai take out of all Thai take outs. In truth Guy was very abstemious and Alexa and I just pigged out! Eventually when we felt certain that I wasn't a danger to our pregnant friend Estelle, we headed back to bed. All that time I was pretty anxious as I was terrified that I was going to be told that we had done something wrong or should have done different treatments. I had put all my faith in the Prof and his team at St Barts and just couldn't bear to hear that it was misplaced. The concept of uncertainty really played on my nerves. The oncologist, a wonderful bear of a man called Stephen Gruenstein, whom I just wanted to hug all the time, wanted to delay giving us an opinion as he suggested that he put my case forward at a meeting of all the leading oncologist specialists from the Sloane Kettering and Mount Sanai Hospitals as my diagnosis (having the two cancers) was unusual and complicated.

So we waited with baited breath and stayed on with Henry and Estelle, who took us down to the beach at

Long Island for the weekend to try and calm our increasingly frayed nerves. The results of that conclave were not what we had expected. We genuinely thought that the American opinion would be in line with Prof Lister inasmuch as I should start further chemo instantly. However, although they agreed wholeheartedly with the treatments I had already undergone, the decree was that I should 'watch and wait', if I could handle it mentally. We thought they would want to attack with all guns blazing. But they didn't. This was because huge strides were being taken in stem cell research. Already there was some success in Seattle (which Debby had said she would be happy to back me to do but I had already rejected as too far away from home and the family – and somewhat more importantly because of the high death rate). This was my best chance. Watch and wait: I just had to buy time for the stem cell research to be more successful. So that is what we decided to do. No more uncertainty. We had a plan.

Don't get me wrong, I knew how fortunate I was to have this opportunity to seek a second opinion, not only from a different hospital but from a different country and from this lucky stand point I say this: find a way. If you need a second opinion or help, seek it. Don't let this wretched disease make a victim of you.

Get your local community to do a charity fundraiser for you if necessary. Go to the local newspapers or radio stations and ask for help. Get your workplace to raise money for you. It's easy to say but don't be too proud to ask for help. Everybody backs a fighter. I have met cancer patients on retreats with Burgs who found this disease had helped them make new friends; neighbours came around to cook for them and helped them with their shopping or just visited to talk with them for a while. On one occasion Atalanta's school raised huge awareness and money for one of their pupils who fell sick with cancer. It is possible. It's not easy but it is possible.

We returned to England having decided that we would continue to 'watch and wait' for as long as I could. Professor Lister respected and was perhaps even interested in this course of action from a scientific point of view. His abrupt, old-fashioned manner belied his deep regard for each and every one of his patients. I cannot begin to say how safe he always made me feel even if he was delivering bad news. He was frank and honest, never beat about the bush and the fact that 'the Americans' knew about him and his research papers only reassured me further that I was in the best hands possible in the UK, even if I did want to deviate somewhat from his suggestions.

Every month his team at St Barts did tests on me, so we knew the cancer was getting worse but the point was that it wasn't yet critical and the chemo would have been. Although it was a rather high stakes game, the more time we could buy, the more likely it was that science would have found a solution for me. Or I might manage to heal myself with alternative treatments.

Watching and waiting. This is easier said than done. Every few months something would go wrong, a new lump would appear and then have to be chopped off, if it was in a place where that could be done quite easily. (That pleased the Professor as then he had more material for research!) Some of the tumours were deep in my abdomen so could not be cut out. This had its own complications: if they grew too big they could impact on my organs and then in turn cause other illnesses. Every time I would be terrified that I'd blown the whole thing and missed my 'window of opportunity', but I never gave up and just kept on waiting for science to catch up while trying to heal myself in any miraculous way I could.

Under this sword of Damocles, our lives started to take on an air of everyday normality. With some cancers you don't feel at all unwell but I did. I felt completely rung out, as if I was battling through porridge. I got bad headaches, which could only be assuaged by jumping on my baby trampoline. We had done this out at the clinic in Thailand and it was agony to begin with but, extraordinarily, after a while the lymphatic system would be jiggled around enough by the bouncing and would process the toxins and the pain would abate. Of course I could have taken pain killers but in a somewhat masochistic way I needed to know what the pain was up to, then I could gauge how serious it was and if another trip to the hospital was required. I rested for two hours every afternoon. That way when Martine left for the day, I was on best form to have fun with Atalanta and Marcus and enjoy the bedtime routine of bathing and reading a bedtime story. If I didn't rest I just turned into a desperate case, screaming and shouting at everybody because I couldn't find another way of coping.

I also started to get better at meditating. Which was lucky, as into the melting pot came Tom. I love Tom as if he was my own son, but he has his own wonderful mother, Diana (to whom I am also very grateful as she looked after our dog and her puppies when I was too weak to be able to cope). But when he parted company with his school it wasn't the best timing. Or so I thought at the time.

That summer term of 2004 Tom spent most of his

time with us rather than at school, frequently banished for some misdeed or another, and by the end of the term it became very clear that he wasn't going back in September. Six foot four and a giant man-child of seventeen and a half, it was decided that home with us was going to work better than home with his mother. With hindsight I would say it was the best thing that ever could have happened and a blessing in disguise. The bond he forged with his brother and sister is amazing. Our family became a fortress of love, which may well never have happened if he had just continued to spend half the holidays and half the weekends out of school. Nowadays he is so busy and I get really sad if he doesn't come home at weekends for a long time. But back then it wasn't so easy being the stepmother to a cross teenager who felt abandoned by his school, as well as trying to stay on top of this wretched disease. Step-parenting. Wow! Now, there's a whole different subject which I should have read up on and didn't (we all laughed when my stepfather did, bless him).

But love gets you there in the end and a few helpful hints, which I am happy to pass on.

If trying to admonish a six-foot-four teenager, make them sit down while you stand so that you can look down at them.

It is hopeless trying to give someone a bollocking when you are looking up at them.

Threaten to throw their clothes/possessions — well, in fact anything that smells and is on the floor in their bedroom and shouldn't be — onto the rubbish tip and then eventually carry out the threat. If nothing else, it makes you feel a whole lot better. (Note: try to make sure that it's not smouldering before throwing it all on as it is not a particularly good look leaping around trying to retrieve burning, smelly T shirts when you really only wanted them out of the house, not burnt to a cinder!)

Try and find a neutral space where you do not give him a bollocking and you are both on an equal footing. In our case it was the kitchen where we would have fun cooking together, and working out what could be good to eat with what. Tom is now an extremely fine professional chef and I am so proud of him. It was obvious from the very outset as he was so talented in just guessing what ingredients would go with what.

Blub so much to your brother (George) about the injustices of being a stepmother with a husband and stepson who seemingly gang up against you that he loses the plot and tells you to stop being a victim and to do something about it and to help stepson learn to manage his time better, get more of a routine going and get boundaries.

Buy a diary. Give to stepson and have daily diary sessions so that you both know what is going on when and where and if necessary with whom. Discuss all college work even if they think you're barmy. Threaten to throw jug of water over stepson if not up at 8.30 am and down eating breakfast before 8.50 am diary session.

Love stepson to death and try to be accepting.

Try not to be too nervous a passenger when helping them learn to drive!

Make sure stepson has chores/responsibilities that help run 'the home'.

Exercise stepson.

That'll do it. As a result of these nine simple steps you end up with the perfect stepson who comes and looks after you when you come home from the auto stem cell transplant a shell of your former human self.

CHAPTER 6

A Note on the Buddha and Meditation

Meditation was helping me stay on top of every day life under extreme circumstances. However, I believe that it was doing much, much more than that. I have had the chance to meet people who have cured themselves from chronic diseases such as cancer. It can be an extremely powerful tool. I never perfected the art to such a level but it certainly was a valiant part of my artillery in living with cancer. Somebody told me that to fail is not to try and that was a powerful message. The very simple act of trying was very empowering.

I have always been a spiritual person, brought up in the Christian faith but I've never been much good with organized religion. Christ was clearly an extraordinarily enlightened being. Who else could say, 'Forgive them, Father, for they know not what they do' whilst nailed to a cross, waiting to die, having withstood extreme torture? Talk about no sense of self. In that one sentence is the very crux of the matter: 'for they know not what they do'. He had total compassion for his murderers because they were 'not knowing', ie ignorant of things as they truly are. But how to find that understanding and compassion in oneself?

I was trying to find this path through Burgs's teachings. All his courses are based on the Dhamma (the teachings) of the Buddha, which is the title of the 'Awakened One' or the 'Enlightened One' given to Siddhartha Gautama, a prince born in about 583 BCE into the ancient Shakya clan in the foothills of the Himalayas. A few days after Siddhartha's birth, a holy man prophesied that he would be either a great military conquerer or a great spiritual teacher. His father, the king, preferred the first prophesied outcome and raised his son in great luxury and shielded him from knowledge of religion and everyday human suffering. Having reached the age of twenty-nine and full of curiosity for the world beyond the opulent palace, he asked a charioteer to take him on a series of rides through the countryside. On these outings he was shocked by the sight of an old man, then a sick man and then a corpse and, sickened by the stark realities of old age, disease and death. Finally he saw a wandering ascetic and the charioteer explained that the ascetic was someone who had renounced all worldly goods and sought the way out of suffering. Deeply troubled, he returned to the palace but found no contentment even when his wife gave birth to a son, who was called 'Rahula', which means 'fetter'. Increasingly he realised that he could no longer bear the luxuries of palace life as he reflected on old age, sickness and death and one night he shaved his head, changed into the clothes of a beggar and fled the palace.

Siddhartha began his path to enlightenment by seeking out all the renowned teachers of the time. But still even after they had taught him everything they knew he realised that their paths only temporarily stopped the causes of suffering but didn't break the inherent cycle of suffering, so he and five others left to go to the forest to find enlightment for themselves.

In order to do this they attempted to find release through physical discipline, enduring pain, holding their breath and fasting to near starvation. Still Siddhartha found no solution and came to the realisation that having known extreme luxury and pleasure, he had replaced it with extreme pain and physical suffering and that there had to be a Middle Way. He realised that instead of starvation he needed nourishment for strength to be able to build up the discipline of his mind and that it was through this discipline of the mind that he would find the path to liberation. With that realisation he accepted a bowl of rice milk from a young girl. On seeing this, his fellow ascetics assumed he had given up the quest and abandoned him.

One night (celebrated in May) Siddhartha sat under a sacred fig tree, now forever known as the Bodhi Tree and settled into a deep meditation and made the determination not to move until he had finally cut off all desire, aversion and delusion and thus reach the deathless state known as Nirvana (or Nibbana) where the cyle of suffering is extinguished. Nirvana literally translates as 'Blown Out'. Just before dawn, Siddhartha Gautama realised enlightenment and became a Buddha.

At first the Buddha was reluctant to teach because what he had realised could not be put into words. He feared that without clarity of mind and insight, listeners would be stuck in conceptualizations and would misunderstand his teachings. However, after much reflection he decided to go to the deer park in

Isipatana, in what is now the province of Uttah Pradesh, and find the five ascetics who had abandoned him and see if they could understand his teachings. It is there that he preached his first sermon, preserved as the Dhammacakkappavattana Sutta, having decided to teach a path of practice through which people can realise their own enlightenment for themselves. The Eightfold Noble Path.

The Buddha devoted the rest of his life to teaching and became reconciled with his father, wife and son. When dying at the age of eighty his last words were, 'Behold oh monks, this is my last advice to you. All component things in the world are changeable. They are not lasting. Work hard to gain your own salvation'.

One step at a time. That is what I was trying to do.

I didn't rush to the library to consume every written word on Buddhism. That is not my way. But I did try to understand the book by Walpola Sri Rahula, *What the Buddha Taught*. I have read it so many times now and still it unlocks more doors every time I pick it up. Page eleven was a major breakthrough for me and I shall quote from the text as it really helped me start to shed my attachment to my ego:

… Elsewhere the Buddha explains this famous simile in

which his teaching is compared to a raft for crossing over, and not for getting hold of and carrying on one's back:

'Oh Bhikkhus, a man is on a journey. He comes to a vast stretch of water. On this side the shore is dangerous, but on the other it is safe and without danger. No boat goes to the other shore which is safe and without danger, nor is there any bridge for crossing over. He says to himself, "This sea of water is vast and the shore on this side is full of danger; but on the other shore it is safe and without danger. No boat goes to the other side, nor is there a bridge for crossing over. It would be good therefore if I would gather grass, wood, branches and leaves to make a raft, and with the help of the raft cross over safely to the other side, exerting myself with my hands and feet."

'Then that man, oh Bikkhus, gathers grass, wood branches and leaves, and makes a raft, and with the help of that raft crosses over safely to the other side, exerting himself with his hands and feet. Having crossed over and got to the other side, he thinks: "This raft was of great help to me. With its aid I have crossed safely over to this side, exerting myself with my hands and feet. It would be good if I carry this raft on my head or on my back wherever I go." What do you think, oh Bhikkhus, if he acted in this way, would that man be acting properly with regard to the raft? "No, Sir." In which way then would he be acting properly with regard to the raft? Having crossed and gone over to the other side, suppose that man should think: "This raft was a great help to me. With its aid

I have crossed safely over to this side, exerting myself with my hands and feet. It would be good if I beached this raft on the shore, or moored it and left it afloat, and then went on my way wherever it may be."Acting in this way would that man act properly with regard to that raft?

'In the same manner, O Bhikkus, I have taught a doctrine similar to a raft – it is for crossing over, and not for carrying.'

Sitting patiently and silently on the mat Burgs taught us to use our body as that raft. You can start to see things clearly as they are (and I mean really as they are), you start to let go of your conditioned views (opinions, if you will), your bad habits and stop being centre stage. You let the universe take over. Attachment/craving and aversion/disliking are the two baddies and it is incredible how attached one is to views and opinions that we build up in our memory bank. If you break it down to its most simplest level, it is through fear that we can reject and decide to dislike. But where does this all come from? What makes your heart beat faster with fear or what makes you feel safe inside? That memory creates an 'energy', a 'force'. The only way you can change that memory and its energetic hold is at a 'software' level. If you cut open the body, you can't see the 'memory' that makes you feel good or the memory that makes you break out in a sweat. It's not physical matter or 'hardware' that you can touch. We know from our very own life experiences that it exists and yet it's intangible. People who have lost limbs often talk of the pain they can feel in the limb even though its no longer there. You can't just decide to override it and change your mind about being frightened in lifts (for example). You have to change it at a deeper level. Burgs calls it finding the root cause.

So with the healing meditation, you calm your mind, and very carefully strengthen it through discipline with mindfulness and 'one-pointedness', to the stage of being able to use it as a laser. Then with this laser you go into your body and start digging up the memories stored there in the cells. Then you attempt to neutralize the energy that the memories carry with them, whether good or bad. You want the middle road: equanimity. Equanimity is rather like getting your pH balance perfect. Neither too acid nor too alkaline. The perfect environment for your body to heal itself.

The by-product of this concentration and deeper awareness is physical and mental emotion and pain! As you penetrate deeper into your subconciousness so more memories and the aforementioned attached 'energy' comes to the fore. If you turn your focus back to the emotion and pain you set off another set of chain reactions, hence why you only look at them objectively, seeing them rise and pass just like everything else in this universe.

At times there is also bliss; just go and see Gian Lorenzo Bernini's *Ectasy of Saint Theresa* in Santa Maria della Vittoria in Rome and that sculpture says it all. But likewise, you have to see it for what it is, impermanent. It's like peeling away the layers of an everlasting onion!

Over time you become 'equal-minded' and cease to be directed by your endless thoughts. You 'step out of the way' (temporarily the ego is no longer activated, the thinking mind that never stops dashing about in an undiscplined manner) and you can start to see yourself disintegrate and evaporate into nothingness: just the rising and passing of cells at one with all living matter. The first glimpse at the breaking down of self.

This is something that Burgs had stressed early on. When I blacked out, he said, I had stepped out of the way. I have always rather admired Burgs's likening the mind to a tethered goat. The goat will frantically pull on its tether going the furthest it can this way and that. But eventually it will realize that there is nothing to gain from this activity and slowly stand and be still. In this stillness the body can start to heal.

Then one fine day you realise that your body is your raft that has helped you cross the river but that you don't need to be so attached to it that you carry it around on your head having finally crossed! That is when your meditation starts to progress.

CHAPTER 7

Don, Mother and Cameron

I smuggled Walpola Sri Rahula's book into one of the retreats that Burgs held at a rather unusual place just outside Henley. Burgs does not have a venue so he rents various places as and when he needs them. I mention it only as even the venue taught me a lot. It has since been sold to a private owner but it was a big house, purporting to be built by Sir Christopher Wren with gardens done latterly by Capability Brown. Into the mix came army quarters from the Second World War when Polish Soldiers fleeing the Germans were given refuge along with their families. After the war a Polish Catholic religious order bought the property in order to house and open a school for all these Polish refugees and it was from them that Burgs rented our rooms in the military quarters, alongside a huge hall centred with an enormous crucifix.

It was an unusual sight (every morning seeing that Christian crucifixion and then Burgs's shrine with the Buddha. Open mindedness, tolerance). The Second World War army accommodation was not exactly comfortable but it was shelter and it was clean. (Forebearance). The plus side was walking down to the river every morning and seeing the rather handsome rowers training every morning!

Last but not least was going up to the main house to eat. Even though you have taken a vow of silence for the retreat, life in the dining room was anything but quiet. Tables of merry Polish people, some from the religious order, others guests or workers (who knows? We could never ask them!) would be feasting and chatting happily. Into this mix we would come and it was easy to become transfixed with this buzz of activity. It was a great diversion from what we were setting out to do, even riveting at times when you set up all sorts of scenarios as to who was who, who was with whom, who was talking about what. You name it, after a while you will do anything to try and avoid the task in hand, ie digging out bad energies stored and locked in your body and relinquishing unhelpful patterns of the mind.

It was here that I met Louise, who became a great friend and fellow warrior of the Big C and, eventually, my guardian angel. George asked me if I could come and talk to a lady who needed some help. Louise was the mother of a friend of both Burgs and George. She had been told that she had six months to live and not to bother to book her holiday tickets to the Caribbean in the spring as she would most probably not be there for the trip.

Her son had suggested that she work with Burgs and learn his healing meditation and that I was a pretty good example of how he could help. She was brave and determined, and a committed Christian who was very happy to seek miracles in any shape or form and from any quarter. With George we discussed what I had done and was continuing to do regarding supplements and diet, and how Burgs had totally changed my life with Eastern medicines and also what Western treatments I had undergone.

Louise had been operated on and advised to do palliative chemotherapy. She decided to do this and while following Burgs's teachings, embraced the 'cancer diet' – all the supplements, the lotions and potions, the juicing … well, everything, in fact, and, amazingly, she went into remission. She loved that holiday in the Caribbean and didn't look back. We ended up on quite a few retreats together. It was so empowering seeing her each time, still in remission … I became quite envious!

Another retreat venue where we used to go was a place near the unusually named village of Horrabridge. In fact the village is very pretty, situated on the edge of Dartmoor but I have to say it conjures up images of some terrible massacre in a 'C'-rated movie. One of my fondest memories is walking with Louise on the last day of a retreat when you have all broken silence and are talking far too much (with the end result being a blinding headache). A number of us had walked up to one of the Tors. It was a beautiful day with views stretching as far as the eye could see. We both clambered up these rocks like excited children, buffeted by the wind, stretching out our arms as far as we could and just letting the sun's rays massage our bodies. We turned to each other and smiled radiantly and agreed that this was 'a good-to-be-alive day'. I honestly couldn't have wanted more: it was perfect. I have forged some very deep friendships on retreat and most of them are based on only a few hours of chatting, the bond coming from somewhere far deeper than words, found in silence.

Coming off retreat was never very easy as I had not yet found a way of bringing my harmonious mind into my everyday life. Sometimes I just went and spent a night alone in the office flat in London so I could re-adjust to the outside world before launching back into full-on family life. But life was sweet, even if there was a great big black cloud hanging over our heads. The children had order going to school every day, Tom went daily to college and I meditated in the mornings, did life's chores and slept for two hours in the afternoon, while Guy worked flat out to keep us fed and housed. Every week I would drive off to get healing from Christa. What was remarkable was that she didn't even touch you. I would sit across the room from her and she never even moved. Incredibly, I would start to feel all sorts of things happening in my body and sometimes would be so overcome with acute tiredness that I would just fall asleep there and then. Weekends were full of family lunches and Don coming to spend Sundays with us. She looked after my siblings and me from the day my older brother was born. She was our rock. If any of my siblings wanted to see Nanny, they just came to Sunday lunch. She was such a wise old owl, not worldly but wise. She had an incredible ability to just sit and 'be' and to listen. I feel so blessed that my children have been able to grow up with her in their lives. When she decided to stop driving we bought her car off her and gave it to Tom and then Tom would go and collect her. These were happy times. In fact, Guy and I are pretty sure that at that time we even said that something had to give, as we were so happy. And it did, but not in any way that we could have possibly imagined.

It was a beautiful July evening in 2006 and we had planned a barbecue. Tom had invited four or five friends for dinner and we had just started. The phone rang and it was Tara, Guy's niece, crying hysterically down the phone that her mother, Guy's only sister, Kim, had collapsed. She was being rushed to hospital in an ambulance with her husband, Geoff. Tara, aged sixteen, not surprisingly didn't understand what was happening. One minute her mother had been cooking supper for her and her sister Tilly and the next she had collapsed to the floor unconscious. Guy tried to calm her and said he would find out what he could and phone her back. Nobody in his family knew exactly what was going on and Guy's parents were driving over to Hampshire as quickly as possible but there was an air of confidence that it would all be okay. In fact she died shortly after arrival at the hospital. How can that be? How can a beautiful, wonderful mother and wife just collapse in front of her children and never be seen alive again?

Kim was so vivacious and so very full of life and

energy. She was a truly fantastic mother and was loved and adored by many. Maybe she was so gregarious because she had to battle with five brothers to be heard or noticed when growing up. Who knows? I feel I am trespassing as I cannot begin to honour Kim's memory in words. Every clever adjective in the dictionary would fail miserably to convey an image of her beautiful spirit. The horror of her untimely death was only magnified by the fact that only a few years earlier her and Guy's brother Giles had been shot and killed in Kenya. They say that there is nothing worse than a parent having to bury their own child. My parents-in-law have done it twice.

Guy retreated into himself. Everyone was in shock. It was made more difficult by the fact that for a long time nobody really understood what she had died of exactly. To this day I am not sure if Guy could tell me. Her heart beat was irregular and suddenly the brain stopped sending messages for it to beat. Ultimately, it doesn't matter. She had gone.

The pain was so great for Guy and I didn't really know what to do except hold him and hug him tight. Guy is an extraordinary person; he's like a coconut palm on a Caribbean island that can nearly be swayed to the ground by the annual hurricanes but somehow has the ability to stay rooted by allowing the winds to rush through its branches, rather than be uprooted by trying to absorb them and remain rigid. However, his perspective on life could not help but change and indeed it did. How can you not help but find the boring mundane inconveniences of life inconsequential?

Sometimes this could be construed as disinterested but it's not, it just seems off-the-radar trivial. In fact we both started to find it difficult to relate to other peoples' lives at all. I can see why journalists covering wars or atrocities committed by hideous regimes find it difficult to return to 'everyday' life. It must seem impossible: the chasm becomes unpassable. You end up saying those ridiculously old sayings that went out with the arc like 'best foot forward' or 'one step at a time' or 'just put one foot in front of the other' and, you know what? That is exactly what you do.

My problem was that I felt tremendous guilt. This sounds so self-centred that I am even embarrassed writing it down. It seemed so utterly awful that I had survived when it was so blatantly obvious that if anyone was going to 'check out' it was more than likely going to be me. Grieving is so strange as you can end up stationary, stuck in a painful time warp. Meanwhile life keeps going at its heady pace and cancer cells keep multiplying, even if you don't want to think about it and only want to nurture your heartbroken husband.

Life had become happy again up until that sad, sad day and the mind has an amazing ability to lull you into a false sense of security vis-à-vis a chronic illness. Our overwelming grief for Kim somehow made it all the more imperative that I should work harder at getting rid of this ghastly disease.

We started plotting and planning a second trip out to the Far East to see if I could beat it once and for all. As always, Guy was incredible and even though he was half drowning in his own grief, we started to prepare for me to go away again for more healing. Somehow it was all just starting to feel selfish. He was the one that needed taking care of. Maybe taking some form of action, maybe that feeling of doing *something* was needed.

Since my last trip to Thailand, Burgs, George and some business partners had created and built a healing retreat called the Golden Rock out in Bali. Burgs had done a lot of healing work with his teacher, Merta Ada, out in Bali before he returned to Europe and he wanted to create a place of his own out there. It was decided that I should go the following spring. The Professor and his team continued to say that I needed to consider further treatments and I continued to say I wanted to delay. They would counter that with the 'you could lose your window of opportunity' line but after Kim, we realized that you really didn't know what was just around the corner.

What was the biggest setback? Money. It's such a nuisance. No wonder it was always considered rude to talk about it. I find it a *very* rude subject. My family are very fortunate and we want for nothing in life but that doesn't include all these weighty extras. So, what to do? Mother was amazing and said she would help us and yet again Debby was incredible and gave me another aeroplane ticket. I would be going for a month but Atalanta and Marcus were so brave and seemed to take it on the nose. They had the stability of Martine and Kim, our housekeeper, and Guy is the most amazing hands-on father. Not only that, our friends continued to be incredibly supportive and would ask them for lunches at weekends so Guy didn't have to cook and the children had friends to play with.

This time around I was actually looking forward to going away. It is very hard to describe how drained I felt all the time. It really is as if a vacuum cleaner is perpetually sucking out your life force and not even sleep can re-invigorate you and so often I had really quite bad headaches, which I was loathe always to medicate. I think I have already said that the best way to stop them was bouncing on the baby trampoline. Agony to start with and I would bounce clutching my head moaning, but after a while the bouncing would jiggle the lymphatic system around and the pain would ease.

The other strange thing to mention is my smell. I stank like a polecat (not that I have never actually smelt a polecat). Maybe it was just fear but I have since read that there is research being done to detect cancer with sniffer dogs. So the departure date was set and I flew to Denpassar in Bali where George met me as he was working at the retreat centre at that time. We got into his car and drove for a three-hour beautiful, if long, car trip to Golden Rock on the north-east coast of Bali near Mount Agung. I was mesmerized by the lush, green jungle and the vibrant towns and villages we passed through.

I was so thrilled to be able to experience all this with George. It is a very big part of his life and I felt so lucky to be able to discover not only Bali, a place he adores, but also to see for myself what Burgs and he had built and created. Not only that but I was going to be able to benefit directly from all their hard work. Boy, was I in for a surprise.

It was absolutely beautiful. Set on a steep slope right down to the sea, it is a compound of several individual 'villas' around a swimming pool, with a small temple at the top and another small temple on an outcrop of rocks in the sea with the island of Lombok visible in the distance. The treatment rooms are at the top and the 'dining area' at the bottom. So you are taking quite a lot of exercise walking up and down steps without even thinking. I quickly settled in. The pool became my base, until the sun became too strong and from there it was easy to go to do the various treatments and head to the 'dining area' for the lotions and potions.

An example of one of the healing programs at Golden Rock is the 'Ten-Day Clear Light Cleanse and Rejuvenation Program', which consists of a seven-day bowel cleansing program including the following:

- psyllium and bentonite bowel cleanse drink
- papaya and/or coconut water breakfast
- raw food salad lunch (maybe avoided for stronger cleanse)
- broth soup tea
- magnesium oxide bowel flush
- nutritional support
- Javanese herbal medicine
- pro biotics
- nerve-releasing massage
- healing massage

- reflexology sessions
- ozone therapy sessions
- infrared sauna/trampoline and Zen chi machine
- biomagnetic therapy
- liver flush
- coffee enemas
- pro biotic flush
- liver cleanse shake
- Monitoring and daily counselling sessions incorporating mediation, yoga and chi kung.

I was there for four weeks so my programme was specified particularly for my needs, which in turn would change if Burgs thought it appropriate. So I settled in and spent hours looking out to sea waiting for dolphins to jump out of the water, which they did now and again. I became mesmerized by the local fishermen. These men are extraordinary wise men of the sea. Their small fishing vessels were hewn out of a single log with stabilizers on either side and hand-sewn sails (some very worn or ripped) and there must have been at least one hundred in our bay pulled up along the beach, and the same, if not more, in the bays surrounding us. Just before dawn they would all set off in the dark, only a few with lights, and head for the fishing grounds under sail, not once crashing into each other. They would return mid-morning and be greeted by the women folk and children and take their catch of a few fish back to the village (and presumably on to market) and then repeat the process again late afternoon, returning only in the dark, always to their same spot on the beach, again, only under sail, never crashing into one another.

Very occasionally you heard the phutt phutt of a very weary engine but never once the sound of wood on wood as they collided. No hats, the bare minimum of clothing in that scorching sun and seemingly no food or water whilst they were out there. A relentless hand-to-mouth existence and if I went down to the beach their smiles would have lit up a city; very humbling. My adversity was lotions and potions, no food, except broth and a timetable of various treatments, none of which were as bad as at the Kwan Jai … hoorah! My journal of this time is much happier than the previous one. Frankly, it was wonderful. Of course I missed Guy and the children and the telephone reception didn't really exist so I would balance precariously on a rocky outcrop with waves crashing about me trying to get one bar of reception or climb to the top of the hill only to see my text fail to be sent. If anything I felt guilt as it was

Guy who should have been there taking time out to heal his wounds.

Now, if a friend of yours says that they will come out and visit you, you don't really believe them but are touched that they appear to be so supportive. And so it was that my very dear friend Cameron said he would come out to Bali. And indeed he did. For three days! I don't think he knew how far away it is! Lunatic! I love him for that mad and crazy trip. He had been there at the outset of this whole journey joking with me that I wouldn't have to shave my head like Sigourney Weaver when my 'alien' was removed … well, we got that wrong! We first met when I was studying in Paris and he was starting out as a lawyer in the film industry. He has conquered a life-threatening illness and is probably the only person in the world with whom I can have really ridiculously negative conversations. Many a time we have dined together and found ourselves being stared at by neighbouring tables as we howl with laughter over hideous near-death scenarios or ghastly hospital experiences as we try to compete with each other. Yes, he flew all that way to come and see me. I still can't quite believe it.

He even managed to charm Burgs! Together the two of them took great pleasure in tormenting me, eating delicious delicacies that had been made as offerings by the villagers and the personnel working for Burgs. Goodness only knows where George was. Probably at the internet café working or at the Blue Moon having a milk shake (another ritual torment for me). I had such a wonderful time with Cameron. He was the first friend who really tried to understand what I was doing, so much so that he would really spar with Burgs trying to understand (and disagreeing) how meditation and holistic healing could help. We talked for hours and it makes me smile so much at the memory of it all as it would have frankly been much easier to have met up for a weekend in England at some spa but, no, he came to the north-eastern coast of Bali. If that isn't friendship, I don't know what is.

There were four or five other people doing detox and healing programmes but we each had our own villa and so pretty much kept to ourselves. When we did meet up in the dining area, which is a bit of a misnomer, really, as we rarely actually ate solid food, all we did was talk about food, which just increased the torment.

One person, who must have found the whole thing rather odd was Darius, a charming gentleman, in the real sense of the word, whom George and Burgs had originally met whilst meditating in a cave somewhere in northern India (random, I know, but that is what happened) and who had been living as a Buddhist monk in isolation in the Thai jungle for a year and a half. He had recently de-robed and come to Golden Rock as a halfway house. He helped us with our yoga and chi kung in the mornings, which became increasingly important as your body starts to seize up as you detox and you start to get aches and pains in places that you never thought were possible. When we all met up in the dining area and ended up talking 'cordon bleu' cooking, he would smile benevolently at us and then with his beatific grin spread across his face tell us how he used to forage in the jungle and beg daily for food. No, it didn't help but yes, we did all fall a little bit in love with him! He never said as much, but for a recently de-robed monk, it must have been tricky to hang out with girls in swimsuits and wraps.

My journal of this time in Bali is so upbeat that it is almost unnerving. And it doesn't even mention the progressive battle with all the steps up and down from the treatment rooms, the swimming pool area, the villas, the dining area and the yoga/chi kung area. At the beginning, you leap up and down those steps with the agility of a gazelle. Then you wander into the sea, when you have a break from treatments, and snorkel at your leisure, looking at the extraordinary array of coral and fish that can be found all over Indonesia. However as the days draw out you get weaker and weaker until it becomes nothing short of a Herculean task to get up to the treatment rooms with the others almost cheering you on as you 'take on the steps'. Likewise, the sea has quite strong currents and getting out of the water requires quite a bit of strength and concentration, otherwise you can slip on coral and hurt yourself. You don't even think about it to begin with but slowly you realize you are not strong enough to do it and abandon the idea altogether, flopping hopelessly under a parasol beside the pool unable to concentrate on anything.

By the afternoon everyone was back in their villa either feeling wretched, exhausted or just hot. As time passed we became accustomed to the slow pace and quite accepting (a huge part of the programme) but for those who came for short cleanses it was entertaining (and distracting) to watch them pacing like a caged tiger, totally unable to switch off and 'find the gap'. There is one passage in my journal that I think is worthy of mention: 'I am beset by restlessness. The mind is rather like an unknotted blown-up balloon rampaging around a room. I look forward to it finally falling to the ground, emptied of all air and activity.'

So the days progressed. What is fascinating to me is how relentlessly we can cling to things that are well in the past and have no bearing whatsoever on our present or future. Our minds can still trigger all the same feelings and emotions from long ago. The cycle simply starts all over again. I still spent many hours sobbing with shame and self-loathing. Sometimes not even understanding why. It's easier said than done, 'just letting go'.

Burgs noticed everything but would leave you to go through all your 'stuff', only quietly coming up to you after the meltdown to see if you needed to talk anything through. Another interesting point was the fact that I just didn't lose any weight (until the last 4 days). Eugenia, a friend whom I had got to know a bit on retreats, was working with Burgs, trying to heal her multiple sclerosis on a ten-day programme; she had to stop her fast early as she was shedding so much weight but oh no, not me. It's so interesting to see how different we all are. Clearly not only did my mind cling on to things like a limpet but my body too. For three and a half weeks of virtually not eating I did not lose a pound and only seven pounds at the end. The clinging mind is like a moray eel – once it bites it is extremely difficult to unclench its teeth without ripping the flesh because of the angle at which they are set, which I hasten to add we saw on one of our 'day trips'.

Burgs suggested we went snorkelling in one of the

fishermen's boats and so, armed with two masks between four of us, we set off. My main concern was that my bottom wouldn't fit in the gouged out part of the boat but in fact that wasn't the problem (the getting back into the boat when you haven't got much energy proved to be nigh on impossible and the cause of several big black bruises).

We set off full of excitement, like children on a school trip, missing lessons. The marine life out there is truly amazing but it became quickly apparent that we were all far more interested in grabbing a mask off each other to check out which fish looked best to eat! Slowly but surely we had become obsessed.

By the time I left there was a big shift in my way of thinking. I no longer anticipated the dramatic healing that I have been fortunate enough to witness in others. Before, I had been the zealous believer, convinced that I could 'pull this one off' and rid myself of this disease without further use of the battery of Western drugs. But now in Bali I found peace in the fact that I probably wouldn't. I shed a lot of the fear and that in itself was a small miracle. I returned home happy with where I was at and pleased that I had got to May 2007 having avoided further crippling high-grade chemo treatments. I had got through nearly five years.

CHAPTER 8

Patti, Goris, Brian, Verity, Michael and Nicky

When I got back from Bali the joy of seeing Marcus, Atalanta and Guy for Easter was immense but it was definitely different from the first trip out to Thailand. I was less hysterical about seeing them. I was calmer and less needy. I think I was beginning to understand that I was able to exist without them. I love them more than life itself but it was no longer in a 'clinging on for dear life' kind of way.

When Guy and I got married, we asked Camilla to read a passage from *The Prophet,* by Khahil Gibran, about marriage.

Then Almitra spoke again and said, 'And what of marriage, Master?'

And he answered, saying, 'You were born together, and together you shall be for evermore. You shall be together when the white wings of death scatter your days. Aye, you shall be together even in the silent memory of God. But let there be spaces in your togetherness. And let the winds of the heavens dance between you.

'Love one another, but make not a bond of love: let it rather be a moving sea between the shores of your souls. Fill each other's cup but drink not from one cup. Give one another of your bread but eat not from the same loaf. Sing and dance together and be joyous, but let each one of you be alone, even as the strings of a lute are alone though they quiver with the same music.

'Give your hearts, but not into each other's keeping. For only the hand of life can contain your hearts. And stand together yet not too near together: for the pillars of the temple stand apart, and the oak tree and the cypress grow not in each other's shadow.'

I have always particularly loved the idea of the trees: both need to be there to be part of the wood but they are individual and must not crowd each other or shade each other from the light. Otherwise they will kill off their life source and be of no use to each other at all.

I think I was beginning to stand on my own two feet and stop being dependent on others. I was no longer the orchid living off a tree, but a tree myself. Did this have any effect on the cancer? Who knows. The power of positive thinking? It's all well documented. Most importantly however it was having huge effects in how I was leading my life and that in turn had to be having a knock-on effect with those nearest and dearest to me. Whatever the outcome of my journey was to be, these days were going to be packed full of love and happiness, not desperation.

The following months were very much like the preceding months. Frightening moments when another lump would appear. Rushing off to the hospital, checking to see if the aggressive lymphoma had returned and I had 'missed my window of opportunity'. Another little bit taken off if it was possible but on the whole I trundled along happily doing yoga, jumping on the trampoline, seeing the kineseologist, seeing Christa, doing my pills and potions, keeping a good diet, resting every afternoon and being with the children as much as possible. I had slipped a bit with the eating and was eating meat and occasionally drinking wine.

Slowly but surely I was accepting that I wasn't going to be one of those people who can get better without Western medicine. For the other kind of medicine to work, I needed to head for the hills, really dig deep and abandon life as I knew it for as long as it took. I just couldn't do it. I had too much attachment to what I had around me. I had walked to the edge of the precipice but I couldn't take that leap of faith and jump.

In a way that realization was a help. I started to accept my limitations and be OK with that 'failure'. I kept on delaying treatments but it was now based more on fear than from a deep conviction that I would be able to heal myself. I went on my retreats, every three or four months (depending on school holidays), and started broadening my horizons with different subject matter now that I was more proficient.

One of the retreats was on the subject of 'loving kindness' and this made a huge impact on me. It was a longer retreat and so we had philosophical discussions in the evenings. I was a bit out of my depth and didn't really add anything to the pot but it was fascinating listening to some very learned opinions. It helped me to absorb the teachings and deepen my meditations.

Despite never having been very quick on the uptake, I am not one for giving up and have always plodded along, one foot in front of the other. You can boil it all down to one simple point: if you do not have love for yourself you will never be able help others in a non judgemental and compassionate way. This turned out to be one of my most difficult retreats ever. More and more shame and self-loathing emerged while I sat on that mat. At one point I came face to face with the realization that I was deeply ashamed of my very existence. I was retching and sobbing, with this ball of shame, anger and a hatred that I could taste, all wrapped up in a ball of burning – well, nothingness. It was like a difficult labour, getting rid of that vile energy. The physical pain was immense and then it just went.

And then one morning the sun both literally and metaphorically started to shine. I was walking in the field in front of the house and came to rest beside this old, lopsided, half-dead oak tree. Most of its branches were dead and either gnarled or broken but there was one part that was thriving still, completely alive and thick with leaves. Even in its rather sad and sorry state, it was still completely and utterly beautiful.

I had an epiphany. That tree was me. So imperfect and yet exactly as it should and only could be with whatever had happened to it over time. Cause and effect. It couldn't be any other way and nor could I. Bingo. Another penny dropped. Finally: acceptance.

It wasn't so very long afterwards that one of the tumours in my abdomen started to make itself known. More tests, more scans and the stirrings of an auto stem cell transplant came to the forefront of the Prof's conversations. By sheer bloody mindedness I had broken through the five-year barrier since my treatments in 2002. Essentially, this showed that the aggressive lymphoma that had gone into the bone marrow was showing promising signs of being consigned to history. As such, it meant that I could do a treatment using my own bone marrow and the stem cells thereof, rather than a transplant from an outside donor. This was the treatment that four years previously I had been advised that I could try, with an outside chance, in Seattle.

This was a revelation. This is what I call a miracle. The miracle of science. The success statistics had improved radically in the five years and many fewer patients were dying (bizarrely that is exactly what they told me when I eventually signed my hospital agreement form) and not only that, the Prof was doing it here in London so I could do it in the comfort of my home patch.

In brief, the treatment consists of a course of chemo (approximately six months) and a course of a relatively new drug called Rituximab, which I had just missed five years previously, to arrest the other lymphoma. After that, if you have gone into remission, there is a course of injections to boost the growth of stem cells in the bone marrow. These are then harvested and frozen and you are subsequently 'nuked' with very high-grade chemo. This is in fact a polite way of saying 'given a fatal dose'.

As the cells in your body all start to die off the stem cells are re-introduced into your blood and hopefully start multiplying. The timing is of course quite important. They warned me that from what limited data they had (the treatment had only existed for a few years), nobody had stayed in remisision with contaminated bone marrow such as I had. No matter, it was my best option to date.

I realize this is hardly a scientific description of an auto stem cell transplant, because, if I tried, I would assuredly get some essential fact wrong. I never really did know the ins and outs of it as by that time I was so exhausted by the perpetual onslaught of disease that I was ready to just succumb to whatever they told me to do.

I can't really remember if this all came to light before we went on an amazing holiday with Debby. She had organized a trip for her birthday in February and invited us. We are more than just a little bit blessed that Guy's birthday is the day after hers! Once again Debby's air miles came to the rescue. She has always led an extraordinarily privileged life but has this humbling ability to understand other peoples' situations and cut through all the bullshit of embarrassment if they cannot keep up; she'll just carry you. Her friendship is deep and sincere. She is an all-or-nothing person. Nothing is too much for her to help you if she can.

When I moved back to London from Paris many years ago, I wasn't very happy and she was the saint who would listen to all my woes, whatever they were. She was the friend with whom I would down a bottle of rosé (or two) when I felt lost and alone. She and her husband James took me in most Sunday or Monday evenings to eat their gorgeous, wonderful 'leftovers' from the weekend. I trusted them implicitly and it was they who introduced me to Lois, when they realised that I needed some help to sort myself out. Actually, she has been friends with my parents since I was three and I still remember vividly the big red sunglasses that she always wore on her head as if they were a headband. Her parents were friends with my grandparents, her son was at school with George and my daughter Atalanta and my youngest sister, Ilona, are her goddaughters. So the bond really is very strong. My mother and my mother-in-law, Verity, agreed to take it in turns to be at home in charge of the children so we left confident that all was well on the home front.

It was everything that a holiday should be and so

very much more. Firstly, it was on an incredibly beautiful traditional Indonesian wooden sailing boat called the *Silolona*, owned by a remarkable lady called Patti. Secondly, we were with wonderful friends. Thirdly, we were surrounded by an incredible crew that looked after our every whim.

We were sailing around the most magical, little-known islands called the Mergui Archipelago off the coast of Burma and lastly, but by no means least, there was no telephone signal. We couldn't use our mobiles for ten days. The effect was extraordinary in this world of constant texting, googling, emailing and calling. We all relaxed. I was used to doing this when going on silent retreats and, sure, I do not have a stressful job where my senses are contstantly under attack from the microwaves of computers and electronic devices and my mind sabotaged by perpetual questions either verbally or electronically transmitted. However, to the other seven, it was a revelation. As the days passed you could honestly see everyone changing and it wasn't just the tequila! I cannot speak for Guy and nor can I begin to comprehend what those five years must have been like for him. But I could see what a wonderful time he was having and how relaxed he was. I heard him laughing and I realized that I couldn't even remember what that sounded like. We were looked after like gods and loved every single nano-second of that trip ... How do you say thank you for an experience like that? And just when we thought it couldn't possibly get better, it did.

One of the reasons for the trip was for the scuba diving and Guy and I were asked if we would like to do it. I had done it as a teenager with my family and had loved it but that was years ago and Guy had never done it. We became hooked instantly and were doing it twice a day. I just loved being down there. It was like being inside the most beautiful picture you have ever seen. I found it so meditative with the breathing and the weightlessness and the total absorption in what I was looking at. We loved it so much that Goris, the dive master on the boat, suggested we take our diving exam with him whilst we were on board. It was all very exciting, and the first time either of us had had to sit down and do homework in a *very* long time.

One morning there was a dive before breakfast but it was decided that Goris would take Guy and me on a lesson while the others would go on the proper dive with Goris's right-hand man. So we waved goodbye and set off in our own zodiac heading for a shallow area where we would only go down thirty feet to the sea bed to practise sitting on the bottom, taking our masks off and do buddy breathing. This is a rescue technique used in scuba diving for 'out of air' emergencies, when two divers share one breathing valve, alternately breathing from it. I had done what Goris had asked me to and was bumbling about on the bottom having a lovely time watching him and Guy do the same training, when I saw this submarine approaching me. I was genuinely surprised at how calm I was and felt just a little bit like James Bond as it did seem somewhat unreal that there would be a submarine here off the coast of Burma amongst a cluster of islands that had been closed to the outside world up until five years previously.

As it approached I saw it had spots. I mean, it really was *very* close. We were only in thirty feet of water. It was at that point that I started yelling into my mouthpiece and trying to bang on my air tank to get Guy's and Goris's attention as I had only recently seen photos of such a thing in National Geographic and was pretty sure that it was a whale shark. Luckily, they turned to see my commotion and looked up. Yes, up. There we were on the sea bed happily learning to scuba dive and a twenty-five-foot-long whale shark passed above our heads with one swish of its tail. I could have touched it. How blessed can one be? In that moment I felt filled to the brim with a total sense of tranquillity. It was so utterly and overwhelmingly beautiful that I cried into my mask. This was rapidly replaced by such over excitement and jubilation that I thought I was drunk. Even Goris (who seems to spend more time under the water than above it) had not seen one for many years. We were beside ourselves with joy and whooped and hollered all the way back to the *Silolona*. The others had had a pretty but uneventful dive and gritted their teeth as they said how thrilled they were for us! I mean, what was the likelihood of that ever happening? It was unbelievable. I shall treasure that memory for ever. We even passed our diving tests, thanks to Goris!

We spent evenings lying out under the stars without a care in the world laughing ourselves silly over the most trivial of things and for Guy's birthday the crew organized a party on a beautiful white beach on an uninhabited island. With a fire and a host of candles in glass jars all balanced precariously on rocks and in caves a feast awaited us. That night was beautiful and at the end we lit huge Chinese lanterns, which climbed up into the heavens of that star-strewn night sky and Guy wandered off into the shallows and cried for Giles and Kim whilst the crew played their musical instruments and sang their beautiful, poignant Indonesian songs. That night I held him extra tight.

In fact 2008 was a ridiculous year for travel. We went back to the oncologist in New York to see what he thought of the auto stem cell transplant and he agreed entirely with the Prof that I no longer had any room for manoeuvre; the cancer had now advanced too much and I had to get on with it. He hugged me and wished me luck. Now that I know what I know, I know why he did, but back then I just thought how lovely he was and what an incredible 'bedside manner' he had. Also, I think I was just relieved that we had got this far and that I was no longer on the run. I was going to face the storm full on and to be honest, it was definitely a kind of relief. The Prof wanted to start in September but yet again I delayed again until November as Guy's father, Brian, had invited us all out to Kenya to celebrate his son Giles's life and honour the tenth anniversary of his death.

This was a gathering in the true sense of the word. Almost all of Guy's family went. Quite understandably, Verity decided that it was going to be too much for her, so she stayed at home and planned another visit with Brian the following year for just the two of them. Marcus and Atalanta came too and we celebrated Atalanta's reaching the ripe old age of ten as much as we remembered Giles's life. The atmosphere was electric. Brian had taken over the entire lodge at Borana, a beautiful game reserve owned by the Dyer family, where Giles had spent so much time and where his funeral had been held. I had spent hours telling the children how difficult it was to see elephants, having trawled Borana on motorbikes with Giles and Guy years before but as we admired our bedrooms overlooking the water hole in front of the lodge when we arrived, there in front of us was a whole herd of those incredible, majestic beasts. Atalanta and Marcus just thought I was mad! Geoff, Kim's husband, and her daughters Tara and Tilly arrived the day before us and had gone out on a safari and seen a leopard. This really is very unusual and after all their suffering it was very special that the leopard let itself be seen by them. So many friends, so many family members, both Thorntons and Dyers (who have very strong family ties with the Thorntons). It was a time full of emotion.

Life and death in Kenya is so raw. I have carried death around on my shoulder and tried to overcome its power to immobilize you with fear but out in Africa that is a luxury that does not exist. You just have to get on with it as tomorrow you may die. My 'choice' to hang on for dear life waiting for science to come up with some wonder cure for my illness does not exist out there. One day you're alive, the next you can be dead. A shooting. A car crash. An aeroplane crash. Malaria. A myriad of causes. This ability to exist on the edge – maybe that is why I love that country so much. I find it intoxicating. Living in the moment. There's no room for what could have been or what might be. It's just the here and now.

We partied hard. Michael and Nicky had pitched a marquee on Giles's hill, where his funeral pyre had been, and the great and not so good of Kenya rolled up on bikes, trucks or little areoplanes and pitched tents where they could find a space in their garden, with the protection of the elephant fence. There was a huge camp fire as it is cold at night up at 3000 metres in the foothills of Mount Kenya. We had barbeques made out of oil drums, cooked up acres of meat, ate huge bowls of salads in a multitude of colours and drank from a bar manned by an increasingly drunk bunch of friends.

A film had been made about Giles set to beautiful music and was shown on a white cotton sheet hung from the top of a landrover. I doubt there was a dry eye there and many wandered off to the huge rock placed on the hill in Giles's memory to be with their thoughts. Marcus came up to me and said, 'Mama, I don't understand it. I didn't even know Giles but that film made my body feel all strange and then I started to cry. Why?' I confess that I didn't really know how to answer.

The music started with the dulcit tones of the generator in the background and as with all great gatherings, the young swooped on the old and dragged them on to the dance floor and we danced away the night until almost dawn. Atalanta and Marcus were exhausted from the long flight and the excitement of seeing elephants, giraffe and zebra, to name but a few. In time they lay down beside the camp fire. We wrapped them up in sheepskins and they fell asleep for the first time in their lives under the mystical canopy of the African night sky.

We stayed a whole week. Michael and Nicky were truly wonderful to us, giving up so much of their precious time giving us a glimpse of both the tourist and local side of life in the foothills of Mount Kenya. We live on an arable farm and so the children were fascinated by the differences; the sheer vastness of the place, which is not suited to cultivation but left for the wildlife and for cattle grazing. The different type of cattle, and how they are protected from the wildlife with a boy looking after each herd, even sleeping with them at night (Marcus couldn't believe that). The wildlife, which even in the course of one week both children became totally used to, proclaiming one day when I was getting over-excited by a particularly large elephant near the track, 'Oh, Mama, it's only an elephant!' The lodge has a continuous influx of tourists, which Atalanta was longing to work at and most importantly the local village and school and Nicky's workshop. I didn't go with Atalanta and Nicky to the school but I think it was a huge eye opener for Atalanta. However, I did ask to visit Nicky's workshop. She designs and has made all manner of things in sheepskin which are then decorated with the traditional Masai beading. Most of her workers are disabled, having suffered from polio. It is actually quite a shock to see some of the devastating effects that this disease can have, which we just automatically avoid with an immunisation in drop form in a sugar lump. Trying to explain to Atalanta and Marcus in the simplest of ways the hand to mouth existance of many of the Kenyan people and how they do not have the medicines that we take for granted and comparing our welfare state with the lack of any help for those in need from their government and how it is up to individuals to help others, was a poignant lesson indeed.

The rains came early that year so we were also able to witness first hand the dry dust turning to 'black cotton' mud in a few hours, ensnaring any vehicle that tried to take it on. Needless to say, there is always an upside and Michael had to get his tractor out to help someone who had got completely stuck blocking the road to Nanyuki. Everybody was soon covered in this black sticky glue-like mud, which Marcus absolutely adored, although he was quite self concious of the local onlookers. We did get to Nanyuki one day in order to stand either side of the equator, which Marcus announced was, 'weird, Mama. I've got one leg in summer and one leg in winter'.

Perhaps the most salutory memory I have of that trip was one afternoon when we went out in the landrover for a safari drive as it had stopped raining and we were all going to have tea with Michael's mother and collect some of her vegetables and eggs. We passed the ford in the dry river bed we would normally cross to get to Michael's parents and merrily drove around, intoxicated by the beauty of both land and beasts. The heavens opened just as we stopped picking an amazing assortment of wild flowers that had started to bloom because of the rains (another upside) and Michael announced that we had better get going as otherwise we wouldn't be able to cross the river. I was genuinely confused as only an hour before it had been a dry bed but Michael explained that it would have been raining for longer up at the top of the mountain and that the rivers could turn from dry beds to raging torrents in an instant. As we approached the pass we could see that there was now flowing water but nothing that would be a problem for the landrover. But Michael said that it was too dangerous. No sooner said, there was an unrecognisable roar and a crashing, foaming, furious torrent of water came hurtling down the river bed, several feet high, sweeping away anything and everything in its path. We would have to wait a couple of days before we could get those eggs and vegetables ...

On a more practical level we had taken very few clothes and were soon huddled around the fire in the sitting room with all our wet, steaming clothes draped over the furniture, trying desparately to dry them before venturing out on another safari in the landrover. This delighted Marcus, who had discovered a Nairobi version of Monopoly and would pester us to play it while the clothes dried.

They were both mesmerized by it all and Atalanta fell deeply in love with the place and is counting the days until she is sixteen when I have said she can go out there to work. It was a beautiful, special time. The calls of the wild ... I hear them. However, the calls of St Bartholomew's hospital in London were louder and we returned to face the storm.

CHAPTER 9

Philippo, Sam and Jessica

What a difference seven years makes. The chemo outpatients ward was unrecognizable. It was in a completely different building in the hospital on the top floor with light flooding in through dormer windows and comfortable reclining seats with your own television screens. It was like being in club class.

So this was where I was going to spend a lot of time for the next eight or nine months. Some of the nurses were different but Carol was there and so were Philippo and Sam, who had also been there 'last time around'. All of them are amazing people. It must be so tiring working with ill people. Not only is there the nursing but their never-ending tolerance, generosity of spirit and beaming smiles are always there to make you feel safe, if not better. The chemo and the immunotherapy, Rituximab, were every other week and they took about six hours to do so I invested in a small DVD player and several series of *24* and *Desperate Housewives* and got stuck into watching them. Those hours soon passed.

I was so happy to have finally taken the decision to do the auto stem cell transplant and not to have the pain like the previous time that it was all a walk in the park in comparison. In a twisted way it was rather nice 'me time'. The lady would come around with a basic selection of sandwiches and fruit and then I would hunker down again with another DVD. Sometimes it would take even longer than six hours. If the results from your bloods didn't come back from the lab for ages you just had to wait but I was very relaxed about it all.

I was on a mission and nothing could stop me now. I had a plan. There was no longer this long dark tunnel of desperation and uncertainty. I was going to start feeling well. That in itself was an extraordinary concept. It is so debilitating feeling ill all the time and so exhausting simply trying not to 'drown' in the gloopy, syrupy sensation of your life force being perpetually sucked out from you. It was going to get worse before it got better. But this was progress.

The side effects of chemo vary enormously but it's

never nice. You just have to get on with it. It's not going to last forever but having to do it on Christmas Eve was awful.

My friend Jessica was horrified at the idea of me spending the day of Christmas Eve in the hospital and said she would come and sit with me. I was far more horrified at the idea of her coming. Nobody ever came with me to do my treatments. Not even Guy. She insisted she came. I insisted she didn't and, little by little, I became more and more upset about it until, Bang! The flood gates opened and I was hit by a huge wave of shame. I felt dirty and guilty for being ill. I realized that I had never let anyone accompany me because I was so ashamed of needing help either medically or emotionally. I had failed abysmally in being the perfect human and I didn't want anybody to see.

Jessica was wonderful and claimed to understand all my rantings down the telephone and on the day came undeterred. She even had to arrange for her mother to babysit her children before getting back to them in the evening. Not easy the night before Christmas.

She brought naughty foods like muffins and good healthy foods that I was meant to be eating, herbal tea bags by the dozen, magazines and newspapers and settled herself in as if she was poolside at a five-star hotel. We laughed and we cried. I think we amused all the other patients with our incessant gossiping and those hours just whizzed by. I shall always cherish that time we had together. Jess has known me for many years and our friendship has known many ups and downs but she knew me well enough to batter down that huge, high wall of shame I had intricately built up around me. Somehow she knew that even when I was saying, 'No, I really don't want you to come' she had to be there.

After she left, Nick, who works for Guy, spent his Christmas Eve collecting me from the hospital and driving me home in his van to Guy, Tom and the children. There is so much kindness in the world.

Christmas the next day was a riot of stocking opening, happiness and chocolate. Father Christmas always buys Guy and Camilla huge Galaxy bars and the children Cadburys chocolate boxes and before nine in the morning most of it was eaten, washed down with a tangerine from the bottom of the stocking. This festive day was full of love and hope: we all knew the road ahead was going to be hard but there was now light at the end of the tunnel.

I was still working closely with Burgs, trying to stay on an even keel mentally and physically and I had also started to prepare for 'the final push' with the help of a Chinese herbalist. The first time I met him I was completely thrown. It's interesting how one has preconceptions of a person and I certainly didn't expect Michael McIntyre (not be confused with the comedian) to look like a quintessential retired army officer with marroon cardigan included. His conservative appearance belied his razor-sharp mind and profound knowledge of Chinese medicine (he had been brought up in Malaya). Herbs and medicinal plants grew in ramshackled abundance around his idyllic Cotswold house, steeping you in calmness from a past era. Meanwhile, trying to keep up with him and his travels lecturing all over the world was certainly very twenty-first century. The months crept by with my fortnightly appointments at the hospital and daily chemo pills that I could take at home. To sustain the body as best as possible I was still doing the 'cancer diet', meditating, yoga, resting every day and the Chinese herbs, which were boiled down and drunk in liquid form. Burgs was still giving me one of his potions but I had stopped taking any more supplements in pill form as I had completely lost my temper one day with them all and thrown them all away. Toddler tantrum or empowered free-thinking individual? Who knows? By the spring I had finished the round of chemo and all that remained was to see if it had put the wretched follicular lymphoma into remission.

It had.

The next stage was easier. We required a daily nurse to visit me at home to give me an injection to boost the growth of my stem cells. Guy could have done this (into my tummy) but I didn't trust him! The injections are similar to IVF, because while in fertility treatment they are given to produce massive amounts of eggs, in my case they were trying to create stem cells in my bone marrow. The optimism is palpable. You feel like a burgeoning little factory brimming with activity, expansion and hope. Then after the allocated amount of time it was back to the hospital to be 'harvested', ie taken out of your body and stored until the next stage. Nobody quite knows how good your harvest is going to be so you have to do it for two or three days. This entails not moving for a great many hours strapped up to a machine that is similar to a dialysis machine. To my mind it looked rather similar to the cockpit of an aeroplane and I now understand why nurses have to do so much training.

Philippo and Sam were in charge of me and Mother came over from France to be with me. I don't really know why this was so important to me as I was over forty and surely no longer her 'child' but it was truly wonderful that she was there to hold my hand and I think something special passed between us during those long hours in that ward. I really needed her and she came. Sometimes we didn't even talk, perhaps I slept, but she just stayed there beside me and read and it was just unbelievably reassuring knowing she was there for me.

The machine is amazing: your blood is passed through it and is then separated into its various components, red blood cells, white blood cells, plasma and the vital bit (and indeed the smallest), the stem cells. These are treated like royalty and analysed and measured before they are whisked off to be frozen. The remaining blood is then pumped back into you. This is an ongoing process (you don't lie there with all your blood slowly but surely draining out of you). It's an out-and-back-in process minus the 'harvested' bits. Needless to say nothing is ever plain sailing but who needs to know the gory details? I am sure that can be seen on *Casualty* or some other such programme. I do remember somebody giving me the box set of *Grey's Anatomy* to watch and I have to admit that I just could not handle being in hospital watching hospital drama. That was a step too far. Give me action or murder-mystery but not A & E!

The next stages were more serious. I had been so

calm all the preceding months but this was all beginning to take its toll and when Philippo and Sam were going through the time frames for the next step, which would probably mean that I would miss Atalanta as Aurora in the ballet of *Sleeping Beauty*, I started sobbing uncontrollably. The pressure to be bubbly and jolly and putting a brave face on it all was just too much. I was terrified. The curtains were whooshed around me and I just wept and wept with Mother trying to comfort me, saying she would go to the ballet instead. But that wasn't actually the point. Underneath all the bravado I was getting more and more frightened of what lay ahead. The high-grade chemo is a fatal dose. It has to be to kill off all the faulty cells and wipe the slate clean. Unfortunately it is rather like blanket bombing and kills off the good cells as well. Only then can the new stem cells be re-introduced and as the cells in the body die off so the stem cells replace them. Well, that's the theory. To me it was like preparing myself for Death Row with the bizarre twist that it was voluntary. It's harrowing. My second Gethsemane moment.

With all this going on perhaps the best way to handle it was by focussing on what the children were doing. Every summer end of term is full of plays, concerts and exhibitions as a grand finale to the scholastic year and this was no exception. Atalanta was passionate about her ballet and had been given the lead part and I was absolutely determined to be there for her. I was terrified that the auto transplant might not work and that I would die. It was imperative to me that my daughter should see me watching her and should have that memory of her mother being there for her, watching her, applauding her. I felt this compelling urge to somehow make sure that both she and Marcus had enough memories of me that they could take with them through life. I was sure that they were now old enough to be able to remember their mother and I just had to be at that ballet. Fate, as it turned out, was on my side and for various reasons to do with the hospital, the dates of my transplant had to be changed and I was there for every single second of my daughter's fabulous performance. I even helped with hair and make-up back stage at the school. Mother was there and my father, as well as Guy's parents Brian and Verity, my friend Kate and another friend Fi, who said she wouldn't miss it for the world. Atalanta looked so beautiful and graceful. I thought my heart would burst with pride. I left for hospital two days later.

Everything had to be organized with military precision both on the home front and with the hospital. I had to be at the hospital every day, morning and evening, but unless something was wrong, I didn't need to sleep in a hospital bed (savings, I suspect). The theory is that they no longer maintained a patient should be in isolation when the immune system collapses, because for the majority of cases, the infection comes from within. But I had to be very close to the hospital so that if there was a problem I could get there in time to solve it as it would undoubtably be pretty grave. They therefore offered us a room in the hospital hostel where it was imperative that I had a carer with me all the time. I have to take my hat off to those I saw on the ward who did this.

The room was perfectly nice with a hospital bed and a sink and a chair beside the window. The bathroom was down the hall and also a kitchenette if you didn't want to eat out all of the time. (Joke: you feel much too ill to eat.) However the tricky bit came when your carer wanted to get some sleep. The truckle bed had to be pulled out from under the hospital bed and then put up in the only remaining space in the room, which was against the door. This made it impossible to get out of the room to go and pee should you need to during the night. If over time you had any laundry, presumably you had to find a launderette.

The hospital was suggesting that Guy would be my

carer but with the greatest will in the world, Guy and I would have certainly ended up divorced under such constraints. Moreover, there was no way he could be my carer as he had to work his socks off to keep paying all the bills and also be there for the children morning and evening once Martine went home. The alternatives were my parents. Well, you can imagine how easy that was going to be for persons of a certain age to not go to the loo all night because once the bed was up, you had to move both the patient's bed and the truckle bed to one side to open the door. Also, with the greatest respect, I don't think either of my parents and I get on that well to be in each other's restricted company for all that time under difficult circumstances and potentially life-threatening scenarios.

Who else could help? Even if it was a paid carer the idea of being stuck in a small single bedroom with a truckle bed for six weeks was almost worse than the idea of having a lethal dose of high-grade chemo. Guy looked up nearby hotels but the reality was ridiculously expensive. We asked if I could be based in Guy's office/flat in West London but were told in no uncertain terms that that was too far away if anything started to go wrong. Then Guy had a brainwave and started looking into short-let flats. There was a whole building of them across the square from the hospital. They were pretty expensive and there wasn't one available for all the time we would need it. More and more research eventually located another flat that I could move to halfway through. Here comes that famous cry, 'How to pay?' My mother and father said they would help, which was amazing, and I will always be very grateful. But nothing is ever simple and even though this was an incredibly generous act, it didn't solve the problem of who would care for me every day.

I was so worried about worrying about my potential carer that I really wanted to have nobody. I was convinced I would be all right as I was now only going to be a stone's throw from the hospital entrance but Guy would have none of it. It took me ages to finally make the decision to find someone I didn't know, who would be good at being invisible. At least then it could be a blank slate.

When I feel ill I'm lousy company and have a short fuse, so the idea of having somebody around me all the time who I would have to be 'nice' to and 'entertain' was awful. Philippo and Sam had told me that there was a lot of waiting around feeling fairly wretched, but bearably so, but then if I got the slightest of problems, very quickly I would be really ill.

Carers are very expensive and in the end we turned

once again to Debby for help. Yet again she was incredible and said she was only too happy to foot the bill as long as she didn't have to do the interviews! I must have done something extraordinary for her in a previous life because sometimes it's just too difficult to understand such generosity and kindness. The conclusion was that we did a number of interviews and I found a lovely lady called Alison.

Finally everything was ready and suddenly, after all these years, the time had come. The storm had arrived. All I had to do was go through it and then I would be on the other side. I wouldn't be on the run from it any more.

CHAPTER 10

Atalanta, Marcus and Alison

Two days after the Atalanta's ballet, Kate came early to take the children away for a surprise 'treat day' so that they wouldn't be there to see me leave. Rather brilliantly she had organized a day feeding and washing the rhinos at the nearby wildlife park. We both hoped that the children, although upset at saying goodbye to their mother, would soon be extremely excited about their expedition. Kate arrived bearing wonderful gifts, such as smelly candles, soap, bath oils, organic moisturizers, magazines and even a really pretty basket to carry it all in order to make us feel that I was going off to a spa and that this was nothing particularly out of the ordinary. She was so amazing the way she just scooped up Atalanta and Marcus with a resounding cry of, 'We mustn't be late for the rhinos!' And with that they left. I remember still that agonizing feeling of loss and fear as her car vanished in the distance with the diminishing faces of my children waving frantically at me, tears streaming down their faces.

Guy couldn't take me up to London for work reasons and so we asked my father if he could take me. My stepmother Penny decided she wanted to come to London and then George also asked for a lift so in the end with all their luggage my father told me I couldn't fit all my belongings in the car. I was in an extremely anxious state and found this very difficult to cope with along with the fact that my father was getting rather cross about being late. Perhaps I minded so much as I needed to feel in control and wanted to keep hold of some familiar possessions in my soon-to-be-strange new home. Thankfully in the end Guy managed to squeeze it all in for me. It was an uneventful journey but I had forgotten my water in the muddle of trying to fit my luggage in and I didn't want to upset anyone further by asking to stop to buy some.

Drinking water all the time was the only way I could keep my headaches at bay. My take is that it flushed out the lymphatic system all the time and got rid of the zillions of toxins which ultimately caused the headaches. I hasten to add that I have no idea whether there is an ounce of truth in this theory but it worked for me. The downside of course is that you need to go to the loo all the time. Anyway, along with the trauma of saying goodbye to the children, crying and the lack of water my head felt as though it was going to explode by the time we got to the rented flat and I felt absolutely awful.

Alison had already moved into the flat and so I was dropped off and 'signed into her care'. Nesting didn't take very long even though I had brought DVDs, photographs, books and groceries and it soon became apparent that Alison was rather amazing at being invisible and quiet, but there if you wanted her. By evening one I realized how incredibly fortunate we were to have found her. She really was my guardian angel and knowing she was in the next door room had a hugely calming effect on me and I felt as safe as I was ever going to feel in this rather surreal situation.

Sleep is difficult to come by in these situations and not made easier by having a bedroom window overlooking Smithfield meat market, which seemed to come alive at about two in the morning with a clashing and a clanking of lorries, lift trucks, carcasses, vendors and general hubbub and which abated at about nine, when the rest of the world was raring to go. I think it is safe to say that at that time I was not particularly interested in the fact that this is one of the few remaining markets left in London and therefore rather wonderful. When we moved into the second flat a little further away from the meat market, we had to walk through it and in the end I felt so ill with the smell of the raw meat that I just couldn't go near the place.

There were still tests to be done; were my lungs strong enough to have the treatment? Were my bloods in good enough condition? A time of controlled fear, waiting for blast off.

On 8 July 2009 I started BEAM. This is the high-grade chemo named after the first letters of each of the chemotherapy drugs. Its aim is to blanket bomb the body, destroying any lingering cancer cells in the bone marrow and killing off all the stem cells that make all the blood cells. The first day of Beam is called Day Minus 7 and then it is countdown until Day Zero when your harvested stem cells are put back in you. It's all very NASA, actually, except there is no actual blast off so all rather anticlimatic if the truth be told. Having said that, I am beginning to feel really very strange as I sit here writing. There are butterflies and wave upon wave of a tingly feeling like the prelude to pins and needles followed by surges of heat coming up from my lower abdomen. The heat is extraordinary. My teeth have clenched and my eyes feel leaden. Both sides of my neck are suddenly seizing up. My heart is racing and my skin has become all prickly. It will all pass but I think we can safely say that this is not a state of inner peace.

By Day Zero we had had to move to the second flat, which was conveniently in Hatton Garden (the diamond district of London) and if anything was going to brighten up my day, it was looking at diamonds in all the jewellers' windows. Various dear friends came to visit me and of course Cameron came too, bringing with him a good luck mascot of one of my bronze figures that he had bought from me. She is called 'Hope' and was very apt. I think they were all rather disappointed that I looked so well!

However, the night after I had been re-infused with the stem cells, Mother, Guy, Debby, James and I celebrated at a Thai restaurant. We were all in such a good mood as everthing seemed to have gone to plan and I was still feel remarkably well. By the next morning though all that began to change.

I began to feel rather ill. At first I was embarrassed to say anything to the doctors and nurses as I thought

I had overdone it with the Thai food and had got a bit of 'Delhi belly' but after a couple of days of feeling really wretched and then throwing up over the cereal Alison had just given me for breakfast, I mentioned it as an aside to the doctors. Anyone would have thought I had announced I had the bubonic plague. I was instantly (and I mean instantly) put into a side room and bloods were sent off. Even my professor would not come into the room as it transpired that I had one of those hospital superbugs and he could not afford to be a carrier, passing it on to another of his patients. Once again I was neutropenic and had no white blood cells (literally none) and therefore no neutrophils, which serve as the primary defence against infections.

I was put into isolation at breakneck speed as I had contracted Clostridium difficile, otherwise known as 'C' Difficile, which can be fatal if you are immuno-suppressed as I was.

Very quickly I became very ill indeed. Mother and Alison took it in turns to be around at visiting times. For a few days I believe it was very serious but fortunately the antibiotics worked and I started to rally. Once I was stable, I was allowed more visitors and Grant's office was nearby so he would pop in to see me, telling me news of the outside world and I do remember my cousin Emma coming to see me. That was quite a feat as she really is terrified of all illness/doctors/blood etc.

Another act of extraordinary kindness was that of Joanna and Mark, with whom we had only recently become friends. Joanna had a rather successful cooking business and her husband Mark was very successful in the city and they had commissioned Guy to do their garden in the country. When they heard of my plight in hospital, Joanna painstakingly cooked me delicious fresh broths every day and got Mark to deliver them to the hospital every morning before he headed on into rather important board room meetings at his bank.

Back in Cirencester, Don was also doing her bit having prayers said for me in her church every Sunday and at her prayer evenings that she and her friends organized in their homes in the evenings.

What I have remembered is that my hair only fell out now after the high-dose chemo and not when I started the chemo in autumn 2008. I had to ask Alison to shear it all off as once again it was awful having these fists full of hair falling out all the time on to your pillow or into your food and drink. I was in isolation for two weeks. I really had the stuffing kicked out of me and could no longer even bathe by myself as I was too weak.

Mentally, the 'C' Difficile bug was difficult as well, as it is so shaming. At first I thought I must have dysentery, which I know only from books and films. But without going into too much detail, you have a very high fever and lose all control of your bowels.

When you are immuno-suppressed the problem is how you get better. You have nothing with which to fight the infections and the vast quantities of antibiotics can't necessarily do all the work so I was extremely lucky that they worked for me. I was told by one of the nurses that in a room next to me there was a patient who was still extremely ill with the superbug after eight months. No, it didn't make me feel any better. It put the fear of God in me.

The nicest surprise of all was when Philippo and Sam came to visit me from the day ward. They work so tirelessly and bothered to come and find me when they were off duty in the labyrinthine maze of hospital wards. My room was miles away as there are not many single rooms for isolation. Seeing their faces popping around the doorframe really was a beacon of light.

Ilona, my youngest sister, came to visit me and was allocated the task of finding a wheelchair for me as I was getting much better and would soon be able to be an out-patient again in the second rented flat. However at that point I was too weak to walk to my bedroom door let alone to the lift and life beyond. She and Alison worked something out and I broke out! I felt quite afraid. My daily life had become a series of time frames from one set of medication to another, administered by a nurse wearing an apron, gloves, bath cap type hat, shoe protectors and an apron. That was my world. Anything beyond the door that they came through was not only a huge physical endeavour but also a mental one, as I knew my body had no means of protecting itself from all the horrors of the every day world.

Once back in the second rented flat, the days rolled by, each one much of a muchness with Alison pouring me into a taxi in the morning for hospital checks and again in the evening, accompanying me every time so she could almost literally carry me out of the cab with the help of the cab driver. Finding the physical strength to walk, well, stagger, to the day ward was really difficult. I had abandoned the wheelchair as quickly as possible as I didn't want to contend with muscle loss as well as everything else but it was a painful process.

I had zero white blood cells. My bloods were flatlining and only time would get the cells to boot up. I could hardly put one foot in front of the other and it took me ages to dress as putting an arm into a sleeve required a rest afterwards but every day I would endeavour to look the best I could and always put on my headscarf and earrings. I just wasn't going to give in.

It did nearly get the better of me one morning as I sat resting outside the dreaded arched entrance to the hospital with Alison. I just couldn't go on. My body was wracked with heaving sobs and I just kept repeating, 'I can't go on any more. I just can't do it. It's over. I have nothing left to give.'

I was a bag of flesh. My soul had fled. I couldn't go on and just wanted it all to end. That was the lowest point and there really was nowhere to go from there but up and, as night follows day, up I went.

I had transfusions, I stumbled along and one fine day the bloods registered life. It was incredible.

This was just the beginning, as obviously you can't go home in such a condition but now there was a glimmer of hope. Forget that, there were buckets full of the stuff. There was concrete evidence that it was working and that has an amazing effect on the mind. Suddenly there was positivity.

With that however came frustration. So much for the state of grace that I was supposed to have found in my meditation practice. I just wanted to get home, to get back to my life, to get on with my life. Anything to get away from this near-death state. And it was my birthday.

I had so wanted to be home for my birthday. Five weeks away from the children seemed like an eternity. They had been lovingly cared for by Martine, who took them to her parents' house in Cornwall for a week once the school holidays had started. Verity, my mother-in-law, had them to stay with her and took them on a beach holiday to Wales and my mother took them back with her to Normandy. I was so happy that they were having a lovely time but we had made an agreement not to have contact as we all knew it would upset us far too much but sometimes it did seem unbearable not to have any contact with them.

Anyway, I couldn't go home and I was pretty low about it so Guy decided to bring them to London to visit me. I was very worried that this would be too upsetting for them but they wanted to come. I was terrified that I would not be well enough to be 'Mama'. I fretted and worried and of course burst into tears when I saw them, it was all just so overwhelming.

They were as nervous as was I but we soon just cuddled up together and just sat there hugging each other. We sat like that for quite a while, silently exchanging love. Marcus was very silent but slowly and surely emerged from his shell of anxiety; Atalanta was the brave big sister who slowly became calm and still, her panic abating. Guy looked on lovingly. It was just perfect. This great dose of love was everything that I had been fighting for and more. Time stood still for a while and that love just recharged us all. Shuffling, moving and giggling, Atalanta and Marcus produced a cake tin in which was the most beautiful home-baked cake that I have ever seen.

It was a 'rainbow cake'. They had streaked every colour of the rainbow through the sponge so that when you cut it it was like a kaleidoscope. It was my technicolour dream cake. There was so much love and hope in that cake, my heart is fit to burst just thinking about it. What's more, they had forgotten it and had had to turn around and go back home to get it, which they laughingly recounted to me. More presents came out, each one bringing so much pleasure and happiness. And then a purple box was put into my hand. Not just any box, but a jewellery box. Now, it is no secret that I absolutely adore jewellery. From a two-euro ring on a market stall in the south of France to one of the Queen's tiaras, I love it, so this was more than just a little exciting. Goodness only knows how long it took Guy to pay off getting these made, for inside my beautiful purple box was the most exquisite pair of diamond earrings that he had commissioned from the jewellers across the street (who incidentally and quite by chance had made my engagement ring). One from Atalanta and one from Marcus and all thanks to my wonderful, loving husband, Guy.

It's not often that I am rendered speechless, but this was one time. When I was better I went to thank the jewellers. They told me how Guy had rushed in saying that they had to help him as I was really ill and needed something beautiful to pull me through. Every time I wear those earrings, we all get rather excited. They are our family talisman.

It was hard saying goodbye, but now that my body was starting to 'boot up' I was confident that I would be home in ten days or so and so we clung on to the fact that it wasn't for much longer. Those days took forever. Each time the doctors and nurses thought the results would be good enough for me to go home there was a setback. Patience is a virtue and it is one of which I am in short supply. But the day did come when they all finally said I was well enough to go home.

I could walk without assistance to get into a taxi now. It was very strange saying goodbye to Alison. She was going off to another job straight away. We both hoped she was going to be able to come by and visit but sadly it has never happened and maybe that is the life of a carer. She was so unstintingly kind and caring and then she was gone. I wish you well, wherever you are, Alison, and I thank you so very much.

CHAPTER 11

Tom, Louise and Dr Hilly Harvey

Home sweet home.

Never was the word 'sweet' more applicable. My good fortune had not abandoned me and Tom, who had decided to leave his job working in a restaurant in London, agreed with Guy that he would come and work for us, looking after me and cooking for us all. He would give me all my medications and be in charge of my juices and all the household food, meals, the shopping and the accounts. It is wonderful to have a family member take over the role of 'you'. Camilla had been truly amazing the last time and Tom stepped into the role quite brilliantly the moment I came home.

The atmosphere was electric as we were all nervous,

excited and a little bit frightened. They all wanted so much for me to be better and 'all right' and were understandably frightened of my weakened state.

I craved to be the mother I used to be but was also frightened by my own weakness. My first day back was very special. It was harvest time and so a beautiful time to go around the farm on 'safaris'.

We have done this since the children were tiny in a very old 1950s delapidated open-top landrover that used to belong to Guy's grandmother. We have spotted many pink elephants and blue rhinoceroses over the years amongst the hedgerows and it was with gusto that the children announced that we were to go on a 'safari' now. My heart sank as I just knew that I couldn't walk to the car, get in it and then have the strength to hold myself as we bounced along in the 'lanny' but I didn't want to let them down. I was led out to the landrover and I tried my very hardest to hide my fear and trepidation but I need not have worried. Guy, Tom, Atalanta and Marcus had all carried out the much-loved huge green armchair from the kitchen where I spent so many hours of my day and where we all sat when we were poorly and had placed it as a throne in the back of the vehicle. I was speechless. They bundled me up into it and there I lolled while we went roaring around the farm looking for fearsome non-existent creatures. Once again the family was back together again and complete.

It was a long old haul. My brain had nearly shut down completely and I couldn't even remember whether I had taken all my daily pills or not so Guy managed to find a very efficient pill storer from the chemist that was broken down into days of the week and times of the day. Every Sunday evening he would lovingly fill it all up so that we could work out at a glance if I had taken what I should have taken, when I should have taken it.

Getting out of the bath was an epic event and I had to rest in between drying myself and getting dressed as each endeavour was so overwhelmingly difficult. I remember the children asking me to get on the trampoline with them and their fear when I collapsed after four bounces. Every day after that I got on that thing and tried to bounce, increasing it by one bounce a week. However, all this physical weakness was easy in comparison to the mental strain. What started with fear slowly but surely grew into terror. It is difficult at the best of times to describe fear but terror is something quite different. It is all-encompassing and paralysing. It cuts off your breathing and then turns everything black behind your eyes and the shutters come down on your brain and it freezes. Just like on the computer when it no longer functions and the screen just gets stuck. That is your brain. My only way to describe it is like being in a waking coma: you see what is going on around you but you cannot react to it.

I tried so hard to get a grip on it. Getting to the end of our drive was a Herculean task in bravery. It would overwhelm me and I would end up in a sobbing mess, hoping that it would be better the next day and return to bed to rest. Over time I grew physically stronger but even with my meditation I was unable to touch the sides of what was going on in my mind. I sat every day trying to follow Burgs's instructions on whichever CD I put on but I just couldn't do it. I had lost all that I had learnt. I thought it would slowly but surely get better but it didn't. I began to lose my footing on reality. It all became a fearful blur but I could tell no one.

It was like being an addict: I would try to hide the fact that it was becoming increasingly difficult to function. It's alarming how easy it is to pull off 'being normal' when everything is screaming in your head. Like a herd of wild horses stampeding towards a cliff, aware of the mortal danger in front of them, no longer aware of the original reason why they are stampeding but the overwhelming collective energy drives them on regardless. The noise in my head was relentless. It was like having five different radio stations playing perpetually at the same time and whilst trying to focus on what each channel was saying/meaning/singing, I had to try and latch on to events that were happening around me outside of my head and de-code that too. More than just exhausting, slowly but surely it was driving me demented and increasingly throwing me into the dark black vortex of despair.

I had my frequent check-ups at the hospital but felt weirdly detached from the whole process. Did I think I was going to go back to work soon? Yikes! I had been ill for seven years and really couldn't remember what it was like to be well, let alone what it was like to have a nine-to-five job, similar to the one I had had prior to all this mess.

I was really out at sea. I couldn't remember how to be well, to be cancer-free. To be able to go through a day without sleeping for two hours, meditating, juicing, exercising: getting better had been my full time job. Who was I? I could vaguely remember the energy I used to have all those years ago but had no idea how I was ever going to be that 'well' Samantha of yesteryear as she seemed a totally different person from the being I saw every morning in front of the mirror.

After a few months they gave me the news that I was in remission and strangely Guy and I did nothing to celebrate. Perhaps a cup of tea and a 'lets go home and tell the children' but that was it. I think we were totally exhausted and there was no space left for celebration, only hopeful disbelief.

For the children, however, it was a completely different matter. We sat them down in the kitchen and I just said, 'Good news, guys, Mama is now well' and the effect was electrifying. Their eyes widened and as if they didn't dare to hope and they asked, 'Really?'

'Yes' was my reply and with that I do not exaggerate when I say that I saw the heavy, grey burden of worry literally lift from their little, young shoulders and they hugged me for dear life.

Remission means you are better. So I had to start acting as if I was better because that was what was expected of me. I still couldn't do a shop up at the supermarket but felt that I was expected to get a job and so started to enquire about one and at a Christmas lunch with two girlfriends announced that I would start trying to work again in London part time.

Perhaps a few members of the family thought I ought to get back into the workplace but certainly not Guy. I was convinced that in order to 'belong' on this planet that is what I needed to do. In fact I hoped it would make me feel a part of 'life' again. I would slot back into paying my taxes and being part of the workers' great big 'hamster wheel'. I had just spent seven relentless years fighting for my life to be with my family and once given the all-clear, I was trying to find a job in a place eighty miles from where I lived! Moreover, most days I could only just get to the end of our drive before having a full blown panic attack.

I felt guilty. I felt I needed to have a job to be of some validity. To be worthy of having gone into remission. I was feeling guilty about being well. I was beginning to think it was easier to be ill and have the job of trying to get better than it was to be well and not know how to be well and what to do with this gift of 'life'.

I went back on a retreat. Burgs was very kind and allowed me to join in on a three-month retreat for ten days, which George was on. It was at a rather beautiful but run-down farmhouse in Staffordshire that Burgs had rented as a venue for long retreats.

It was freezing cold and we had de-humidifiers in the bedrooms as the place was so damp. I remember sleeping in all my clothes and with two woolly hats as my hair had still not really grown back much. I was joining an already established meditation group, which is not very easy to do, but it was wonderful to be back amongst some friendly faces. It was there on the mat with Burgs helping me that I first started to catch some glimpses of peaceful stillness within my turmoiled, screaming mind.

A long retreat is very different from a short week-long one. There is some talking and reading spiritual/philosophical material is allowed. There are many chores that have to be done during the course of the day and everybody knows what their responsibilities are and goes about them much the same as I would expect monks would in a monastery. In the evenings I would go to George's yurt and sit with him in front of his little flickering fire and we would talk and then do our last meditation of the day together before I ventured back out into the snow back to the house.

My, how I had changed from my first retreat. Now, in total contrast, I felt that being on retreat was the only place I could handle it all. I couldn't cope with the responsibility of children and the most basic chores of every day life. I couldn't make decisions. In the outside world I would walk up and down supermarket aisles and be overwhelmed by the choice available and leave empty handed. In Staffordshire I had a roof over my head, a bed to sleep in, compassionate companions who asked nothing of me, food on the table, wood for the fire, exercises and my mat. In that rarified place I began to feel like 'me' again but it didn't last for long back out in the big wide world.

I did my best to shield the children from what was going on in my head. Sometimes I would just grip the rail on the aga in the kitchen and exclaim that I had to concentrate on the water boiling in the kettle and that no, I couldn't tell them whether I could make a parents' meeting next week, I just had to stay in the 'now'. Then the tears would come and when looking at their worried, frightened faces I would just say that it was all perfectly normal, I just needed to release some 'energy'. They must have thought I was bonkers. They were partly right.

Debby, amazingly, invited us back on the incredible boat we had been on two years previously and in February 2010 we went to the Andaman Islands. Once again, Mother kindly agreed to come over from France to be at home and be '*grandmère*' whilst Martine and Kim kept the show on the road.

Two weeks in a place nothing short of paradise and I really have very few memories of the trip at all. The noise and mental mayhem in my head just shut everything out. It wasn't really actively shutting it out but my mind was so full to overflowing with perpetual panic it couldn't fit anything else in.

We returned to Martine handing in her notice. We had told her at the beginning of the year that Marcus was going to boarding school after the Easter holidays and that her position would then sadly be redundant but I had really hoped that she would stay with us until he went off. Understandably she had found a new position and wanted to keep her future employers happy by leaving sooner than we had anticipated but it's true to say that I was upset. She had been the bedrock of my children's lives during this epic ordeal and indeed an essential source of security for me as I knew they were safe with her so I could concentrate on myself. The end of anything is difficult and this was the end of an eleven-year collaboration on childcare. Needless to say we have remained close and my children can't wait for the holidays so that we can organize a fun day with her and her daughter, Isabelle, but I have to be really honest and admit that when her new job fell through after less than a month I was unsympathetically delighted!

My foundations were pretty wobbly and this was a blow to my stability, losing one of the mainstays of our family sooner than I had mentally prepared for. Lord only knows what it is like to work in such tricky conditions and she always had a sunny smile on her face and a sense of dependable calm around her, which was so important for the children. It was time for me to stand on my own two feet and I couldn't even get onto my knees.

Before she left Martine sewed on all the nametapes of Marcus's smart new school uniform and so his new life started. I had been to see the school with Guy and in my mental haze had thought it was a charming little school with cosy houses for the children to board in. In fact it's one of the biggest prep schools in Britain; the Dragon at Oxford! I'd have never agreed to him going there had I understood. But that was the problem, I wasn't understanding anything. Of course Guy was right and the upside was that Marcus was soon thriving. In fact it was probably an important turning point in his life. He had seen his mother ill for as long as he could remember and now he knew she was better. What better time to spread his wings without having to witness her sobbing, clinging onto the aga rail for dear life. Atalanta was flexi-boarding several days a week and was likewise able to be amongst her peers and not be confined to the solitude of being 'stuck' at home surrounded by fields and a mother screaming that no, she would not, indeed could not, drive her to meet up with her friends.

Camilla, who had returned to England, came down to stay and was the perfect sister, quietly but slowly and surely sussing out the situation and then gently advising me to seek help.

Over the years I had sought so much help from so many sources and had an arsenal of telephone numbers to people that I could turn to but I was too paralysed by fear, even to do that.

The tears that I shed that evening were the beginning of the long haul back to finding me. After she left for London, she phoned me every day to ask if I had been able to put in a phone call to seek help but she never berated me when I said I couldn't. After a couple of weeks it became so normal as a concept that I actually started to entertain the idea of being able to pick up that phone. To start with I didn't really know who I was going to phone if and when I did. The choice seemed too big. Eventually with a little nudging from Camilla, I came to the blindingly obvious conclusion that I should ring Lois, who had helped me so much at the beginning of this journey. I stuck up a post-it in the kitchen with her name and number written on it and looked at it daily. That also became 'normal' and after a while caused me little or no anxiety. In the end, I never did put in the call because when I went for one of my check ups at the hospital it became very quickly apparent to the oncology team that, although I was physically doing well, my mental state was far from good and I was bundled off with a referral to a cancer psychiatrist.

That first visit was pretty frightening. Dr Hilly Harvey was the name of the psychiatrist. Her rooms were in one of the outbuildings at St Barts just near to the wing with the CT scanner. Just thinking of the

CT scanner made me extremely anxious. Everything seemed to fold in on me and suddenly I was finding it very difficult to breathe. I would have done a runner, had the weight bearing down on me not been so huge. Pressing that buzzer with her name on it was so hard. Here was a therapist who specialized in helping cancer patients, who was clearly going to be able to help me and yet I was really, really frightened. How would she judge me?

When I did meet her on the second floor I was sweating so much I was embarrassed to shake her hand. I was panicking and for some reason instantly tuned into 'hostess mode'. I started to have a mild out-of-body experience as I watched myself making polite conversation, noting how she had a ring on her left wedding finger; congratulating her; asking her when she was going to get married ... oh, how lovely I got married in September too ... an Indian summer, most probably ... a wonderful time for the second flowering of roses ... I mean, *hello!*

Mind doctors are amazing people – how they unravel the cat's cradle of knots in our minds. Medical science, I can get: over the centuries, incredible leaps and bounds have been achieved. Indeed, I will reiterate that medical science and science in general are nothing short of what some would call a miracle. The brain and the mind, though, constitute a relatively recent specialized study and we still have so much to uncover. The very fact that we humans are able to build such unbelievably complex computers indicates to me that our minds must, by definition, be even more superior than these machines and that is pretty awe inspiring, but I digress.

Two hours of being assessed, at the end of which I had nearly got through an entire box of tissues, was the start of a new chapter in my life.

I was told that my situation was far from abnormal after such a long time battling with a chronic disease and that I was suffering from something called 'Post Traumatic Stress Syndrome' and had had what is known as a partial breakdown. Once again, like all those years before, I found great solace in giving my situation a name. It was such a relief that it wasn't just me; it was a well-known scenario. I felt like a grateful child. I felt better already! What is that saying? A problem shared is a problem halved.

The next six months were hard graft. We decided that we would try and see if we could work it through without medication as I was almost hysterical at the thought of more pills. Dr Hilly gave me mental exercises which I was to do whilst meditating and then gradually implement them into everyday life when I felt I was able. With hindsight I can compare it to the physical, repetitive exercises my brother Grant was given after his stroke to get his left side working again. This was re-programming. Obviously, if this had not worked we would have had to move on to 'Plan B' and medication.

My mind slithered around like mercury but with these mental excercises I was beginning to be able to rest it on something solid. Yes, this is what one does with mindfulness practice when focusing on the breath but I had just not been able to do it by myself. Over the weeks, using these repetitive mental exercises, my mind started to calm and thus the abject terror started to abate and the panic attacks diminished.

The thing with meditation is that you are trying to purify the 'lower' mind and let go of the ego, abiding in a clear, still state that is always present in the background. My lower mind, aka the ego, was in such turmoil it was impossible to venture through to the stillness but at least I had the tool kit for mindfulness and mental discipline, even if I wasn't able to apply it by myself.

The only way I can really describe my state then is by saying that I should have been the weather man on TV: forewarning the public of a large storm, displaying knowledge and objectivity as I pointed out weather fronts, low and high atmospheric pressures. Instead of which, I had somehow landed in the storm itself and was totally unable to find my way out. Thankfully my weekly sessions were starting to show me the way. I would talk at a hundred miles per hour trying to reguritate what was whizzing manically around in my head. Sometimes I dare say I didn't even make sense but Dr Hilly would calmly stall me and make me focus on a single item which we would then slowly unravel: the tears would roll, the questions became more penetrating and on and on it would go until I gained some clarity, until I reached some form of resolution. Sometimes this meant making a deal with myself that there was no resolution but that was OK. At each session we made charts, grafts, line drawings, diagrams, cloud drawings, you name it, trying to put solid structures on paper so that I could actually 'see' what I was thinking and therefore try to 'see' how I could a) accommodate those thoughts and b) cajole them into new thought patterns. Most of these thoughts were unbelievably dark, hideous creatures that wanted to claim my soul. Thoughts that I was ashamed I could even think. Thoughts that were totally unacceptable for a woman who had fought to live for seven years, who had the most wonderful husband and children and everything to live for, including new-found health. Sometimes I was so horrified by my thoughts that the thinking about the thinking would set off a whole new cycle of suffering.

It was all very surreal and I felt that I was playing this 'life game' of snakes and ladders and had just landed on the longest snake and was back down at the beginning of the game. But if there are snakes, there must also be ladders.

One of the many insights that came to light during this time was that I was as equally frightened of success as I was of failure, which revealed itself when we were trying to unscramble why I started sobbing and shaking when discussing sculpting again. I had stopped a few months before going into hospital. I just couldn't do it any more. From the moment I started sculpting after my first round of chemo it had been my haven and when I was really working in the 'zone', the figure I was making would of course be based on the life model before me. But it also came from within me and the blob of wax in my hand was partly 'me'.

It's not easy to describe but that intimacy of putting my 'soul into it' was impossible for me. Not just difficult but truly unbearable. But not one to be deterred, my sculpture friend Caroline persuaded me that everyone was missing me and to just come to the class and say hello. I physically shook on entering the room and could only stay at the back quietly crying, I know not what for, but the kindness of everyone there, their total compassion and lack of judgment was a tonic in itself and I started going every week again just sitting at the back, getting used to being there and not feeling threatened.

Our teachers Jan and Hywel were so unbelievably patient and understanding and just accepted me as I was. Then one day Caroline asked my opinion on the piece she was working on at the time and without thinking I told her what I thought needed to be done. She made no song and dance about it but just passed me some wax and suggested that I show her where exactly she needed to change things. There was no thinking involved, it was instinctive. I just did it. Layering small pieces of wax where I thought they needed to be put. Such a small thing and yet so monumental for me. There are plenty of artists out there who would never let you touch their work but Caroline is so selfless and so deeply caring that she just wanted to help heal me. I think she is an angel fallen to earth.

Nothing at this time was plain sailing though but darling, wonderful, dependable Guy plodded on regardless. After all this time of being on red alert, and just when we could supposedly relax a bit, the wheels were coming off and flying all over the place. Sometimes I thought I was really getting to grips with everything and other times I just got caught up in that black vortex of negativity. I knew deep down I had to go on another retreat to really work on all the psychiatric stuff and to try and assimilate it. This was agreed by Dr Hilly and Guy and so once more I set off on a trek to try and find that Holy Grail of peace.

As soon as Burgs opened the meditation the morning of day one I started to weep and by the end of the day I was extremely frayed, which was magnified tenfold when Burgs announced that Louise was very ill indeed and held a special meditation session for her in the evening. Louise, as I have already mentioned, had been my friend on many retreats and she and I had battled against our respective cancers together on many fronts. I knew the wretched disease had come back but had been so wrapped up in my own problems that I had failed to comprehend the severity of her situation. That hit me like an articulated lorry and I spent a long and lonely night with nonsensical thoughts whizzing through my head like a Red Arrows display. Why was I alive? What right did I have to survive if Louise was dying? What was the point of being alive if I didn't know how to live? The following morning, after an incredibly emotional first meditation before breakfast, I decided to break all the rules and go to the nearby church. You are not allowed to venture beyond the immediate garden on a retreat. This is for a very good reason. It is emotional work re-wiring your software and it is unwise to venture far when in such a fragile state. However, I had been to this particular venue on retreats many times and knew the lay of the land pretty well so knew where and how to sneak off. Louise was a committed Christian and I wanted to go and pray for her.

The church is about a mile away and to get to it you have to cross a very beautiful miniature suspension bridge over the River Wye. As I crossed it I fancifully thought that this was the River Styx and that I was crossing over into Hades. The setting of the church is straight out of a Jane Austen novel and incredibly beautiful, nestled in amongst fields behind which rises a beech wood. I was deeply troubled and confused and just sat alone in the rather dank graveyard praying for Louise and praying for myself. It was Rememberance Sunday and I was sitting on the monument to all the local soldiers lost in the First World War so I prayed too for all the many men, women and children killed in war. This was not the praying of quiet reflextion but of deep, deep desparation. This was my third and last Gethsemane moment. There was one last brave rose on a bush in the graveyard and I placed it on the

Remembrance Cross and walked back to the bridge, drowning in deep despair and overwhelmed by my hopelessness and helplessness.

The early morning mist was still rising off the river and the sun was beginning to break through on this cold and beautiful autumn morning. I stood for a long while on that bridge, drinking in the beauty of the place and wanting so desperately to be part of it, to be as tranquil as that flowing river.

And then it came to me with such beautiful simplicity: that I could be. The mad, crazy thoughts of my mind slowed to nothing and the noise – that crazy noise of stampeding wild horses – just vanished and it all seemed so wonderfully simple and clear. It was perfect. All I wanted was to be swallowed up by that beautiful ribbon of water: that was how I was going to find peace. Calmly I stepped over the side of the bridge and stood with my toes quivering over the edge, marvelling at the simplicity and beauty of it all. For the first time in such a long while I was truly at peace having reached this simple and yet so blindingly obvious solution and it was blissful. Everything seemed to suddenly fall into place. The clarity was breathtaking. I just needed to get out of the way.

Then another distinct voice within me started to speak: it said, *What the hell are you doing? This is not the solution. That peace you seek is within you all the time. Go to the clear light. Go back to your meditation where you know you can find it.*

For centuries we have carried around the image of an angel on one shoulder and the devil on the other. This was the ridiculous scenario I found myself in in that instant. I saw with terrifying awareness what my 'mad mind' was prepared to make me do. Shakingly, I stepped back over the bridge side and crawled all the way along it to the dry land, literally on all fours, sobbing. I fled back to the house in utter confusion and joined the group who had already started their morning session of meditiaton.

That morning session was a mess. I was all over the shop, trying to make sense of what I had witnessed within me. And then the news came. As Burgs closed that morning session he called for us to give love to Louise who had sadly died at breakfast time.

How could her life have come to a close at the same time as I was battling with mine on the bridge? She was such an amazing woman, wife, mother, grandmother. It was all wrong. I was insane with confusion and ran once again from the house straight back to the church across that dreaded bridge. I sat in that graveyard for over two hours sobbing and talking to Louise. I felt such enormous guilt that she had died after such a noble struggle and that I had so very nearly 'ended it all' at almost the same time, purely because I was so lost. (Actually, in fact I am a very good swimmer so would probably just have swum to the river's bank.)

I cried my heart out in that graveyard and thank goodness it is so remote, otherwise somebody would have definitely carted me off to the loony bin. In those terribly sad hours I told Louise of all my fears of being alive; how I didn't know how to re-integrate into my life, how I felt guilty for surviving. She came to me. That wonderful, beautiful lady came to me as one last good act on earth and she gave me permission to live. In that beautiful, silent graveyard, I made peace with my survival and bade a final farewell to her. I slept at the foot of that stone cross and when I awoke I crossed back over that bridge for the last time and smiled to myself as I realised I was returning from Hades unscathed, all thanks to Louise.

The afternoon meditation session was nothing short of extraordinary. I felt like Houdini. I was able free myself from all my bonds. Everything just started falling away. Louise had given me the key to unlock my prison chains. Not only that but I was able to take a good long look at my 'lower mind' (ego) from a totally objective viewpoint and with great peace of mind I turned to it and said, 'Enough. Go. I see clearly now what you were prepared to make me do and I do not need you any more' and with that there was this physical clunking and clicking within my body as I actively started to turn away from this mess called 'self'. Slowly but surely my body started to disintigrate completely and I became simply the rising and passing of particles, at one with the universe. This blissful state of total absorption. No different from stars, planets, anti-matter, air. Nothing left, just the dying and re-birth of cells. That's all you are; nothing else remains. Coming out from that deep meditation, I was spent and slept again and when I woke up I went looking for Burgs for an interview, as I needed urgently to talk to him.

CHAPTER 12

Sal, Tom, Pat and Sibylla

Severing the ego. Now there's a big one. Perhaps it can happen overnight for some enlightened beings, I don't know. All I know is that it is a long and arduous task: a lifetime's work – maybe several. But you have to start somewhere and at least I had now glimpsed the road ahead. Talking to Burgs was wonderful and very cathartic. There were more tears as I explained everything that had happened but nothing surprises the man. He has so much ancient wisdom. I hadn't talked to him since I had arrived on the retreat and he hadn't seen me since Staffordshire the previous year, so although he was aware that I was struggling with life, he had no idea that things had got so bad.

We talked for quite a while. He had been there helping me since I was first diagnosed and although it is perhaps presumptuous on my part, there is a special bond. There was much to discuss but eventually he advised me to go and lie down and rest. We both agreed that I had been very blessed by Louise's presence and needed to allow my body and soul to now heal.

This whole experience had been so overwhelming that it took the rest of the week on the retreat to assimilate what had happened. The net result though was that I was once again free. The veil of confusion had lifted. My broken mind had not suddenly become unbroken, but I had found all the pieces and Louise's 'visit' had given me the the glue and I was now able to start putting myself back together. There was no doubt about it, it was all rather extraordinary. The stampeding horses had gone. The black vortex of paralysing fear had dissipated. I mean just gone. Vanished. Of course I was in this very rarified environment on retreat and it would be interesting to see what it was like in the big, wide world but the difference was enormous. I felt at peace. Real peace. Everything seemed very clear. The colour of the sky. Touching a stone wall. All my senses were so alert.

I suddenly had clarity in place of the chaos and

could see solutions to very simple problems which had been unbearable to even contemplate only days before. The knots really were unravelling. I was genuinely able to think about things a few days hence. Previously this had caused me real anxiety. Oh, so many little every day things that I had not been able to cope with. I so desperately wanted to be better, the idea of it all being just a temporary illusion was worrying but strangely enough what would have previously caused me a temporary meltdown just seemed a potential set back.

Suddenly there was hope. If I could do it once, then I could do it again. I was alive and it was time to start living.

I returned home from the retreat and went for a long walk with Guy to tell him what had happened. We both cried. It was as if we had been given another chance. I remember clearly walking back down our drive together holding hands with this amazing feeling of a new beginning. We both knew that there would be hiccups along the way but everything was going to be OK. My appointment with Dr Hilly was a few days later and once again I recounted everything that had happened and how I felt and the effect that it had all had and she just looked at me and said, 'You've done it. Congratulations. You should be very proud of yourself', or words to that effect.

What makes people wake up from a coma? Why does the brain suddenly re-boot and reconfigure itself? I'm not sure there are any concrete answers to this yet and I was just very blessed that it had happened to me. That day and the last session with Dr Hilly were of a more practical nature. My thinking processes were very different from how they had been before I was ill and I could easily overload and become anxious but now we put into place exercises/practices that I could do in order to help me out of whatever hole I fell into and, yes, my mindfulness meditation was paramount to keeping everything in check.

Being methodical was key. One step at a time. That way I could keep that sense of being overwhelmed in check. Breaking down instances into bite-size components so that I could deal with the individual portion and not be overwhelmed by the big picture. Cajoling myself into being able to do things by seeing what might happen were I to take action and equally seeing what might happen if I didn't.

This acceptance of various outcomes was hugely beneficial. Being able to see that not doing something is not necessarily failure; just a different route. Being able to see that you can still get to your destination by taking the little roads and not always the motorway was a big breakthrough. For example, Christmas was coming up and as both Guy and I have very big families it is quite a big operation that I had not been able to even consider. However, talking it through with Dr Hilly, we considered doing nothing and what the consequences of that would be. We considered falling back into my old patterns and what the consequences of that would be. Finally we worked out a plan of what ideally I could manage every day in the lead up to the big day and being happy with the idea that the strategy might not go according to plan! It sounds so simple and yet it was momentous.

We worked on seeing life as a continuum rather than a sucession of deadlines that I invariably never made, which inevitably made me feel overwhelmed by my failure. We worked on prioritising. Seeing things in order of importance or immediacy and then not panicking when the whole list of things that needed to be done was not achieved. My sense of time was dreadful. We tried to break down these endless lists I made with disastrous consequences as firstly they ended up frightening me and secondly there was never enough time in the day for me to achieve my goals so obviously it would all end in failure and woe.

We broke down the day into sections, putting in what was essential and then seeing how many hours were left. Armed with that figure, we could then work out realistically what I could achieve. Why did I sabotage myself when I was on time, fitting in something of no consequence that then made me late? We worked out that it's because I like to control the possibility of failure; I create the failure so am not made to feel anxious by potentially failing (ie being late) and then feel more in control.

We worked on my 'envy'. Yes, that green-eyed monster that seemed to rear its head frequently within me. For the most part, it was through comparisons. I was forever comparing myself, my life, my house, my holidays, my bottom, you name it, against others and in the process, always felt inferior ... the grass is always greener on the other side syndrome.

Well, if I looked at a)what I had more closely and b)thought about what others had in some areas but maybe not in others, I came to see that it was all smoke and mirrors. When envy came up I learnt to list what I had been blessed with and I soon started feeling pretty good about myself.

Over and above all of this was my new safety net. Ever since the very deep meditation when I had 'disintingrated' and 'melted' into the universe I felt a sense of ease. That realisation that I was part of the universe, that deep sense of being of the same matter as the universe was extraordinary. It was deeply comforting. When my mind started to spin out of control, I realised that I was no longer 'in the storm' but the weatherman again and could look on objectively and realise that, yes, this was only a storm and that there were much bigger ones raging on Mars or around the sun! Most days I would reflect on the fact the world was indeed going to continue spinning at approximately 1000mph and that yes, planet Earth was still going to continue circling the sun. That helped put things into perspective.

My sessions with Dr Hilly were on the NHS and were coming up for review. We both decided that I was ready for the big wide world but I had the reassurance of her telephone number in my diary and her insistence that I should call at any time if I was struggling. I also had a few 'safety' phrases that I was to look at every morning. One of my favourite phrases is 'it's all right to ask for help'. Another is 'don't muck up good trying to be perfect'. Simple and yet so terribly difficult to do when you're in that vortex of negativity.

In the middle of all this 're-education' was Louise's funeral. Burgs and George came and collected me from home, with a de-robed Darius in tow, who had re-emerged from a temple in Burma, and we drove down to Somerset to a beautiful church where the service was to be held. It was a breathtakingly beautiful ceremony and the first time in my life that I witnessed a Christian service with Buddhist chanting, sung by

Burgs. The church was ablaze with candles, there was light everywhere and at the end when we left there were bundles of spring bulbs that Louise's grandchildren had tied together in sacking for everyone to take home and plant in Louise's memory. It was all so beautiful and such a fitting tribute to such an incredible person.

After the service I introduced myself to her husband, whom I had once met fleetingly. He gave me a hug and said, 'Ah, Samantha, you're the miracle girl that helped Louise so much. Thanks to you, she was able to stay alive long enough to see all her grandchildren born.' I was stunned. It was George and Burgs who had done everything to help her; I had simply helped show the way that I had taken and given her support. I feel so enormously grateful for that generous comment. It was another little piece of my salvation.

I had felt so indebted that Louise had come to me in my hour of need; it felt wonderful to know that perhaps I had helped her too and that the scales weren't so unfairly tipped after all.

Since ancient times the return of the adventurer from an arduous journey has been celebrated by giving thanks. This might be with a feast that includes the sacrifice of a bull to the gods or just a village party with the local bard tied up behind a tree. This is what

I wanted to do. No, not tie the bard up behind the tree (Asterix and Obelix, in case you are not fans of the books); but to give thanks.

Since becoming better, so much had changed. Everything looked different and what had been totally impossible before, now seemed doable. I still very much needed my 'tool kit' and having previously been a very lateral thinker I could no longer do that at all. The mind just seized up completely. I was now a 'vertical' thinker. My thinking could go up and down like a ladder or a lift but couldn't go sideways. No wandering off ... it was important to keep the horizon quite low. If it did, anxiety hit and I somehow had to get back in my box (in my case, meditation or sleep). With Guy's unwavering support and jokes about 'women, know your limits!' whenever I was having a bit of a turn, I finally made peace with the fact that I would probably never be suited to a nine-to-five job again.

But life was good. No, it was great and it was time to shout it from the roof tops.

But how to say thank you? Well, if you sit still for long enough a butterfly will come and land on you and so it is with ideas. In January 2011, after being in remission for just over a year, I decided I was going to raise money by going down the River Thames in my green plastic rowing boat, *Pog*. Guy and the children had given me the boat a few years previously as a birthday present, vanishing early in the morning much to my confusion and re-appearing a couple of hours later with Guy driving slowly down the drive and the children frantically waving their arms behind the car standing on what looked like air as I couldn't see the boat. We had talked for years about having a boat to go picnicking on the Thames. Pretty, it was not. Sturdy, it was. Guy proudly announced that it was almost unsinkable due to its plasiticity and its rectangular shape. It was the boat of choice for lock-keepers.

I was over-the-moon utterly thrilled and it even had my name inscribed on it. My father, Grant, George and Camilla have always called me Pog. When I was young, sometimes Poggy May. None of us know why but that's just how it is.

My father's farm went down to the River Thames near its source and it had been the most wonderful way to pass a happy afternoon when not very strong or well. We would pack a picnic and head off down to the river and spend hours of happiness not really going anywhere or doing anything. It was at the end of one of these very happy days that we were hooking the Pog back onto the trailer at Lechlade when an Irishman, who was working on his barge asked the children why our boat was called 'the Pog'.

'Because it's Mama's name,' was their reply.

'Do you know what it means?' said he.

'No. It doesn't mean anything. It's just her nickname,' they countered.

'Ah, well, you're wrong, young'uns. In Irish it means *kiss*'. After all these years I finally learnt that my family had been calling me 'Kiss'. I still beam with delight whenever I think about it. Needless to say when I told Grant and George they were rather annoyed as they had hoped that it had been an derogatory term in some way. Brothers! I still have fanciful ideas about one day owning a big boat to which *Pog* would be tethered and it would be called *Pog Mo Thoin,* which is Gaelic for 'Kiss my Ass'!

Well, I set my sights on London.

A river is very symbolic: its birth from a spring to a meandering course with rapids and tranquil pools, getting bigger and bigger until it reaches its final destination, where it dissipates into the seas and oceans, seemingly becoming nothing and yet rejoining the giant water cycle of our planet. One day that same water will fall somewhere as drops of rain and once again flow down a river and the cycle will be repeated over and over again. We talk about the river of life and I had fought my darkest demons with a river. I didn't want to end up at the sea as that would represent the end of life's journey. London was two thirds of the way to the sea; it seemed just perfect.

It was to be a celebration of life and its meandering

course. There were days when this seemed so simple and days when it seemed like a Herculean task. It was on one of these days that I was walking with my friend Sal, discussing my somewhat insurmountable dream. 'Would it help if I did it with you?' she said.

Well, she kept her word and did. She leads a very busy life but she found the time to blot out a week in order to do this with me. Yet again the words 'thank you' just don't convey the gratitude I feel. So we had a task: we were to raise money for Professor Lister's research and for Burgs's meditation teaching practice. I dared hope that we would raise £2000 for the research at St Barts and felt uncertain about raising £1000 for Burgs, but those were our goals.

We didn't want to do it in the winter months and trying to coordinate dates meant that the chosen week was 9 May 2011. A date, a cause, an expedition. It was set in stone. All we had to do was tell everyone about it and then do it.

The reality was that I still wasn't very strong so Guy said in no uncertain terms that we would have an engine as well as our oars. There was no point in me becoming critically fatigued and setting off another chain of events to illness just in order to give thanks. The other setback, of course, was that we didn't really know how to row. Paddling around, yes; rowing over one hundred miles, no. Actually, we didn't know how to use the outboard motor either!

We spent hours collating the addresses of friends and family. Tom, Sal's husband, was fantastic and at one point appeared to have his whole office working on our letters and addressed envelopes. The letters went out and Pat at the Barts and the London Charity (the charity for St Barts Hospital) set up a Just Giving page for us. Obviously we had to make it very clear that we would be assisted by a 5cc outboard engine and one hundred per cent of all donations would go to the causes as we were underwriting the trip ourselves.

I was so worried that nobody would back us as I wasn't sure where I was going to find £3000 to hand over at the end of it. How wrong one can be.

As the time approached, the cheques started coming in and it was the most astonishing feeling being supported by so many wonderful people. My bank very kindly set up an account for Burgs's meditation fund but quickly we whizzed past £3000 and suddenly I was being called in to be grilled about money laundering. The joke was that I was flattered anyone should think I was clever enough to work out how to launder money!

Two weeks to go and we were to be seen in the local camping shop buying all the waterproof kit we thought we might need, including waterproof covers for our phones. We had decided we were too old to camp and had provisionally booked rooms in pubs along the way. Of course we were not certain if we would do the distance each day but at least it gave us a goal. For night two Sal's son's school had said they would put us up and night five I cheekily rang up the rather wonderful hotel, Cliveden, and told them what we were trying to do and why and asked if they might like to have us to stay as we couldn't possibly afford their prices. I never thought they would ring me back but they did and gave us an incredibly favourable discount, which was just too good an offer to refuse. We had an unforgettable night there with our husbands. More and more goodwill from people we didn't even know!

Ten days to go and Guy announced that he really thought we should have a practice go at passing through a lock. Up until that moment we had not once practised rowing either alone or together.

We almost capsized just trying to get into the boat and in fact by far the most dangerous thing was the engine. We were worse than useless. I still have a film of us that Guy took with my phone and it is hysterical: we hadn't even realized that we had to row facing backwards! Guy was adamant that we should always use the engine when approaching a lock as that was the most dangerous time with other boats.

So Sal and I approached the first lock on the Thames at Lechlade with fear and trepidation and a certain amount of alarmed shouts from the children as we veered from 'port' to 'starboard' in a totally uncontrolled way.

We nearly capsized. We didn't realise you had to loosen off the ropes as the water is going down in the lock. More hysterical giggles with a hint of panic in them. What would a week be like?

D-Day approached and Sal and Tom decided to have some T-shirts printed, stating our charitable cause with our photos on as well as some very smart flags (though pennants sound rather grander!). This way everybody would be able to see what we were up to and why, without us having to explain ourselves. Friends, family relations and dogs all came down to the river to wave us off. The champagne was cracked open and we nervously seated ourselves in our trusted vessel and set off.

Two minutes later I was flat on my back, laughing uncontrollably with Sal almost invisible in a hawthorn bush that we had rammed into. Things could only get better.

It soon became apparent that rowing together was hopeless. I am almost twice the height and width of Sal and as a result we just went around in circles. So we quickly organized our new home into sections: rowing station in the middle, engine/tiller station aft and 'office' at the bow. We each took it in turns to row while the other did 'office' work forward. This included emergency phone calls for picking up children from school but was primarily to read up about where we were going and where we were.

We were the proud owners of the invaluable manual, *Waterways Guide to the River Thames and the Southern Waterways* (no 7, if you're interested) and *I Never Knew That About the River Thames* by Christopher Winn, a jewel of a book citing every historical fact or legend that you ever needed or indeed didn't need to know about the towns, villages, churches, houses, bridges and fields either side of this wonderful river.

Last but not least I was reading *Three Men in a Boat* by Jerome K Jerome. This was quite confusing as the the story is set going upstream and we were going downstream. My brothers had been very rude about my map reading skills and how unsure they were that we would make it to London but I was pretty confident that even I couldn't get lost going down a straight river. We soon realised that it is more complicated than we thought. You do have to be a bit careful as otherwise you end up down a weir.

Our silliest moment was when confronted with a huge sign of DANGER across the middle of a tributary and an option to turn left, I turned to Sal and said, 'That must mean we're meant to stick to the edges' whereupon we so very nearly ended upside down shooting down a weir. I don't think we stopped laughing that whole week, albeit sometimes rather hysterically.

However, I digress: we were on our way and even had a lunch in our honour to make two locks down. We were at Lechlade and that unforgettable first lock. One hour into our expedition and the heavens opened with a fury. No problem: we had our wet weather overalls from the camping shop, only I appeared to have picked up a jacket for a child. Fortunately we had some black bin liners which I duly stuck my head and arms through for some cover but was drenched in seconds. Not a good start for a compromised immune system.

Nervously we tried to start the engine as we approached the lock. We both nearly fell overboard with the exertion but made it into the lock without crashing into the walls too dramatically. Two girlfriends were there to cheer us on and the lock keeper surprisingly recognized us and dashed off into his house returning with a huge, warm, fisherman's waterproof jacket which he insisted I put on and keep. What is more, he was amazed that I returned it to him after we had finished our adventure. He even gave us money for our cause. And so it was to be.

For that entire week we encountered only the kindest of people. Everyone helped us. Apparently we became known as 'The Two Totties in a Tub' and we began to suspect that each lock keeper phoned the next one downstream to alert them of the imminent arrival of these utterly hopeless, giggling lunatics zig-zagging down the Thames in a very unprofessional manner, as they were most definitely expecting us.

That first day 'Johnny' was our knight in shining armour. Further downstream we ascertained that he was actually called Michael, but we were so convinced that he was our river version of a Johnny Depp pirate that we continued to call him 'Johnny'. It didn't matter, he was too kind to care.

We had seen him and his wife on our practice day; long grey beard, long grey hair in a pony tail and a wonderful array of hoop earrings in each ear. He works on barges, taking them from A to B up and down the river. What a wonderful couple. He worried so much for us that he even gave us his mobile phone number in case we should have any problems. That was just after we had asked him how best to tie the boat up.

We even came across our very own three men in a boat. It was the most beautiful nineteenth-century varnished rowing boat and of course I instantly fell in love with it – the contents weren't bad either! Anyway, river and lock life mean that we kept bumping in to each other nearly every day and so at every meeting we would all discuss our aims for the day and where we were hoping to reach by the end of the day.

They were rather more authentic than us, as they were camping. On the third morning as we passed each other, one of them shouted out, 'By the way, Charles Dean sends his love.'

I nearly fell overboard. Charles Dean had been my 'boy' friend when I was six (we shared a desk at school) and he had been relieved of his position as one of the 'three men' the day before we started our adventure. More to the point, he must have rung up for a low down on their progress and have been told about these lunatic girls out on the river who never stopped laughing and put two and two together, having received our letter, which I had sent to his mother asking her to forward it as we had rather lost touch over the years. Small old world. And rather comforting.

Guy and Sal's husband, Tom (not to be confused with stepson Tom) came to meet us at whatever pub we stopped at each evening. It is a curious thing to travel all day long down a river. The river banks are often high on either side and we found ourselves in a private world with spring exploding all around us in abundance.

By the end of the day it was almost inconceivable that the husbands could reach us from home as, after approximately eight hours of travel, I genuinely thought I was in Asia or the Americas. The maximum we ever did was twenty-eight miles in a day.

It takes less than two hours to go from our home to London in a car. Being on the river distorts everything. We were busy, fully occupied and intent with our mission but totally peaceful. It was bliss.

Friends came to see us either just to wave from a bridge or to bring lunch and an afternoon of boating or a fun night out in a pub listening to our day's excitements. And still the money kept coming. We had an app on my phone that pinged every time there was a donation. We became rather obsessed with it but were wary of the phone ending up overboard so all phone calls and activity were handled with care.

Of course the most wonderful thing of all is the peace and the time. Finally I understood the caption on a card that a well wisher sent me, which is still on my desk as it resonates so much with me: 'Never fly faster than your shadow'. We were going at the pace of my shadow.

Even now I have to be careful with travel. My stepmother Penny is the same and we both put it down to chemo but we don't really know why. Too many hours in a car and we both turn into blubbering wrecks and have to rest for twenty-four hours. Going about four miles an hour and yet somehow feeling that the world was rushing by was absolutely perfect. Sal likes to walk every day so at some point when convenient, or more to the point when we thought we could make a safe landing, she would get out and march forth with vigour to the next lock whilst I rowed and marveled at how many greens there could possibly be in all the foliage around.

It was off season for boats but the river was bursting with goslings, geese, swans, signets, ducklings and ducks in abundance and of course the river bank, which always seemed to sneak up on us so that we crashed into it. When you are facing backwards it is extremely difficult to work out the meandering path of a river. That's my opinion anyway, for what it's worth.

Apart from the locks, we hardly used the motor as we were having so much fun rowing. We never became very proficient at it: for some reason we never quite grasped the concept of turning the engine to the right to go left and vice versa but it did ultimately lead to hours of mirth whenever we did fire her up. Teddington was lock forty-five and after that we really did feel happier with it as we were then in the tidal part of the river and you are meant to know what you are doing!

It was rather strange hitting the outer reaches of London. The river lost her intimacy but with urban sprawl it became busier; it was truly marvellous to see sailing races going on as well as sculling and rowing. The Thames is not very wide and it is remarkable that there is so much sailing. They must be brilliant at tacking.

Needless to say, it was a miracle that we didn't bump into anyone in this hive of activity as we were very unsure of where rowing came into the rule of sail taking precedence over motor. The most embarrassing moment was at Putney when we were regaled over a loud tannoy with the words, 'Green Pog, Green Pog. Do you realize you are in the middle of a rowing regatta?' Mortifiying!

We kept on going to Battersea Bridge, which was our final destination. The waves were getting pretty big (everything is relative) and Sal was sitting in the bottom of the boat so we were relieved to be ending here. This was particularly poignant as my older brother Grant was going to be there.

He had recently suffered a bad stroke and was being treated in the Chelsea and Westminster Hospital near Battersea Bridge. Tom (stepson, not husband) and his girlfriend Annie 'kidnapped' him in a wheelchair (still in his pyjamas) and with their help he managed to get onto the pontoon where we were landing. This was an act of great bravery on his part as he was only beginning to get back the use of his left side but fortunately he is as pig-headed as me and with time would be all right. It was the first occasion he had managed to walk and I hadn't seen him out of a wheelchair since it had happened. We were both survivors. It was extremely poignant. What I had been through. What he was going through. Of course I cried. We both did.

The end was pretty haphazard, with friends and family there to cheer us on and Pat and her team from the Barts and the London Charity clutching balloons, banners and cup cakes. Her generosity and kindness were all the more special as she had hung around all day waiting for us and it was her birthday. Grant even had a donation to give us from a fellow patient from the next-door bed in his ward. That made me cry again!

This whole journey had renewed our faith in the human race. If you listen or read the news too much you can just get brainwashed into thinking the human animal is depraved but in fact wonderful and amazing acts of kindness and generosity are happening all the time. But that just doesn't increase circulation or viewing figures.

We gave a cheque of £12,000 to Burgs, who has been able to restructure his meditation retreats as a result of it and now has a bursury for those who cannot afford to pay for board and lodgings. His teachings have always been purely on a donation basis.

We gave Professor Lister's team (well, in fact his successor, Professor Gribben) £25,000 but with with Gift Aid that went up to £33,000. Our grand total was over £45,000.

So much for worrying about raising £3000. We were speechless, which if you know us, is quite something.

Sal and I were invited to Prof Gribben's laboratory to have a tour and to see the research he and his team were doing. This was all rather exciting as it meant that for once I was going to be the other side of the desk, so to speak. We invited a few friends who had been generous benefactors to our cause and proudly donned our white lab coats on the appointed day.

I have to say that I think it is the first time I have ever worn a lab coat (I felt very grown up). It was rivetting and oddly tiring seeing in detail what was being done by these incredibly clever scientists. It was also a little overwhelming, as ultimately this research was what had saved my life.

Talking with one of the team, Simon Hallam (whom I often saw for my check ups) about his area of research was of special interest to me: his work is specializing in the field of immunology, which was the Rituximab part of my protocol the second time around. He was trying to ascertain the role of cyanide in breaking down the protein coating of the cancer cells, which have an amazing capacity to actually befriend our immune cells and thus stop them from doing their job of attacking the cancer cells. My jaw literally dropped.

Miniscule amounts of cyanide can be found in the Vitamin B17, which Burgs had advised me to take for several years at the beginning of this journey for that very reason of trying to break down these protein coatings around the cancer cells. B17 is found in apricot kernels, grape pips and apples seeds – that bitter taste when you used to crunch on the grape pip before they all became seedless. Based on the fact that the Hunza tribe in the mountainous hills of Pakistan live well into their hundreds and are not blighted by cancer, 'alternative' healers have researched their diet to see where it differed from ours in the West and noticed the increased use of B17 in their diet of apricots and particularly the apricot kernel.

Well, here was Western science scientifically researching what eastern/complimentary/supplementary (however you want to term it) medicine was doing. My two parallel paths were finally converging. The circle was complete.

So what now? I get tremendous harmony and joy from my meditation and yoga. In my yoga group we have become rather caring of one another, a miniature little community all trying to stay on top of our aches and pains. Likewise, when I go on a retreat, we are all so utterly thrilled to see each other if any other fellow longtimers are there, babbling away like veritable fishwives before taking our vows of silence.

I am getting more and more involved with my sculpture and hope to find the courage to have a proper exhibition some time soon but I guess this book is the final piece of the puzzle. Last year my friend Sibylla continuously urged me to write this all down. I thought she was bonkers (well, she is, but that's another story). Slowly but surely I thought, 'Why not? It's a good way to celebrate ten years since I was diagnosed. Even if it's only for my children to read one day.' So I put that post-it up on the wall with 'write a book' scrawled on it and in time felt comfortable about giving it a go.

Ah, Atalanta and Marcus, I don't really know how to convey my luck and pride in being your mother. You are both so incredible. Such wonderful, beautiful beings. My loves, I love you all the way around the universe and back. It has been such a huge pleasure being here, seeing you grow up.

But perhaps this can be of help to others. It has been cathartic, of that there is no doubt. My perspective is going to be different from anybody else's involved on this journey but I hope it speaks to someone.

When Professor Lister retired I cried. I am so indebted to him. I put all my faith in him and he never faltered taking on that responsibility. He made me promise that I would always keep up my three-monthly check ups as he was pretty certain it will come back sooner or later.

Sometimes that becomes all rather overwhelming but, even if it does, medical science is making so many breakthroughs I will probably only have to pop a pill every day. Who knows what's around the corner of life?

It was our wedding anniversary last week (which I had totally forgotten about rather embarrassingly) and Guy gave me this quote from the Buddha, which I think says it all:

The secret of health for both mind and body is not to mourn for the past, not to worry about the future, or not to anticipate troubles, but to live in the present moment wisely and earnestly.

Ultimately I feel truly blessed to have been so loved and nurtured and helped by so many. Love does conquer all.

Printed in Great Britain
by Amazon.co.uk, Ltd.,
Marston Gate.